THE SUN AND ITS INFLUENCE

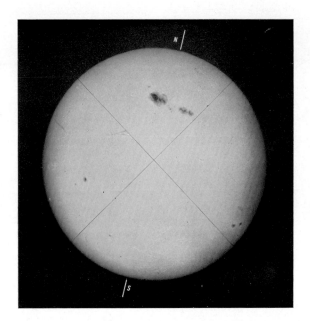

1946 February 5 (Greenwich)

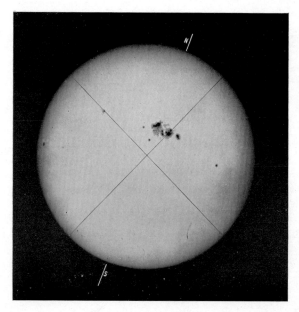

1951 May 16 (Herstmonceux)

PLATE I.—GREAT SUNSPOT GROUPS

(Reproduced by courtesy of the Astronomer Royal)

THE SUN AND ITS INFLUENCE

AN INTRODUCTION TO THE STUDY OF SOLAR-TERRESTRIAL RELATIONS

M. A. Ellison, Sc.D., F.R.S.E.

PRINCIPAL SCIENTIFIC OFFICER
ROYAL OBSERVATORY, EDINBURGH

THE MACMILLAN COMPANY
NEW YORK

This book is dedicated to

MY WIFE

and to those solar workers
who encouraged my early
endeavours, notably :

A. M. NEWBEGIN,

H. W. NEWTON,

F. J. SELLERS.

Printed in Great Britain
by Butler and Tanner Ltd
Frome and London

Preface

IN this book I have endeavoured to knit together recent discoveries in widely different scientific fields, so as to present a connected account of the sun's activity and its influence upon the earth.

I hope the treatment is neither too advanced for those with a knowledge of elementary physics, nor too simple to be read with profit by workers in other sciences. The account is mainly factual; for, in solar-terrestrial relations, as in other branches of astronomy, speculation tends to outdistance verifiable knowledge.

Meteorologists may be disappointed that no place has been found for a discussion of the influence of solar activity upon the lower atmosphere, in terms of weather and climate. Much has been written on this subject and many claims have been made, but most have been refuted by later work.

My grateful thanks are due to many friends who have been kind enough to allow me to reproduce their results, as well as to the editors of the various journals in which these have appeared. Acknowledgements are made to each in the appropriate places. I am also indebted to the editor of *Scientia* for permission to reproduce sections of Chapters III and IV which have previously appeared in that journal. Finally, I should like to thank Mr. W. E. J. Farvis, Mr. D. H. McIntosh and Mr. James Paton— specialists in their respective fields of the ionosphere, terrestrial magnetism and the aurora—who have kindly read over these sections of the manuscript and offered valuable criticisms. The responsibility is mine alone for the views expressed.

M. A. ELLISON

Royal Observatory, Edinburgh.
1954 June.

Contents

List of Plates

Figures in the Text

CHAPTER I

CHAPTER II

CHAPTER III

CHAPTER IV

CHAPTER V

CHAPTER IX

The Sun and its Radiation

INTRODUCTION

THE sun is unique in this respect: it is the one star in the whole universe whose surface we can see. All the other stars, even the nearest and the largest, are so remote that the great 200-inch telescope can reveal them only as points of light. This fact at once singles out the sun as an object of special interest to astronomers; for, the fascinating phenomena which we can see taking place in the solar atmosphere provide valuable clues to the behaviour of the stars in the universe at large.

There are also other reasons why we study the sun. If you are a radio listener you may have heard the B.B.C. announcer apologize because Alistair Cooke's *American Commentary* has failed to come through 'on the air'. Large sunspots have been given as the cause; and you may have wondered how such disturbances, occurring 93,000,000 miles away, can affect the radio set by your fireside. You may even have noticed that such interference is much more frequent in some years than in others. Again, in quite a different manner, the sun may upset the quality of television reception. You may not have experienced this kind of interference, but you probably will in a few years' time when the sun again becomes a powerful radio transmitter. These are simple examples of the influence which the sun's activity may have upon the earth, a comparatively new branch of science which we now call solar-terrestrial relations.

For centuries our astronomical sight has been confined within the narrow band of frequencies to which our eyes are sensitive—just those colours which we can perceive in the rainbow spectrum. But we now know that the sun and the stars radiate other electromagnetic waves extending over a vast range of frequencies. If we may use, by way of illustration, the homely analogy of the musical scale, we may say that with our eyes alone, we can perceive less than a single octave, while the whole wave spectrum covers a range of some ten piano keyboards. Thus, it is clear that our knowledge of the universe has been built up, perforce, by very imperfect means. In the long ages of evolution the eyes of living creatures have been very beautifully adapted to the needs of their everyday lives. Yet this 'bread and butter' vision with which nature has endowed us is a most imperfect instrument for the study of the sun and the stars; it has to be supplemented in all manner of ways.

These extensions to vision have been made in two quite different, we might almost say opposite, directions. First, we have seen the introduction of monochromatic vision, as in the spectrohelioscope invented by Prof. Hale. This is the principle of *narrowing down* the range of sight until we apprehend light of a single frequency, so that we can observe just those waves which are emitted by atoms of one kind, as their electrons switch from one excited state to another. In this way we are able to study at all times the complex motions of the hydrogen gas in the sun's atmosphere. To normal vision the feeble light emitted by the hydrogen atoms is completely lost in the intense glare of the many other wavelengths which reach us from the solar surface.

Secondly, new advances have made accessible a wide range of frequencies hitherto unexplored. Photographic plates and lead sulphide detectors have extended our knowledge of the sun's spectrum far into the region of lower frequencies—the infra-red. But that is not all. In 1931 Jansky in America made the surprising discovery that electromagnetic waves, identical with those of short-wave radio, were reaching us from the Milky Way. By good fortune there is a 'window' in the earth's atmosphere which is transparent to waves in the range of wavelength 1 cm. to about 20 metres. No doubt many other radio waves both shorter and longer try to penetrate but fail to get through. In 1942 Appleton and Hey in England found that these radio frequencies were also being emitted, very strongly at times, by the sun and could be picked up on radar sets. The new science of radio astronomy has developed with great rapidity since the war, and it is already clear that these discoveries are the greatest in observational astronomy since the early years of the seventeenth century when Galileo first turned his tiny telescopes towards the sun and planets.

Progress in the direction of higher frequencies has been no less spectacular. These shorter wavelengths, which we call the ultra-violet, are completely absorbed by a layer of ozone high up in our own atmosphere. Since 1946 many rockets, carrying cameras, spectrographs and radio transmitters, have penetrated well above the ozone layer and have brought back photographs of the sun's ultra-violet spectrum never seen before. Such records will be of great value in the future; for it is this part of the sun's light which we believe has the power of ionizing atoms, that is to say breaking them up into ions and electrons, in the earth's upper atmosphere. The ionized regions—the D-, E- and F-layers of the ionosphere—have the remarkable property of bending back to earth the radio waves we transmit from the ground, so that by their means long-distance radio transmission becomes possible.

The sun's radiation consists not only of waves but of particles. The particles are much more difficult to detect and so we know less about them. Occasionally we can

3

watch them leaving the sun during a solar flare, or when some large prominence cloud is seen to blow off into outer space (Plate IV) at a speed which may be as high as 500 km. per second (310 miles per second). Many attempts have been made, so far unsuccessfully, to follow these corpuscles on their journey from the sun to the earth. None the less, we can easily recognize them—at least those which carry the right amounts of energy—when they approach the earth one or two days later. They produce the dancing luminosity of the aurora borealis, violent disturbances in the earth's magnetism and prolonged radio 'black-outs'. These particle showers are just bits of the sun's atmosphere thrown out by electrical forces. During some of the great solar flares particles have been emitted at much higher speeds, approaching the speed of light. Swift particles of this kind can carry a great deal of energy; they are known to us as primary cosmic rays.

Of what nature is this central star—the hub of our solar system—which is at once the preserver, and the disturber, of our terrestrial balance? What are its sources of light and heat, so lavishly poured forth to maintain our life on earth? How do solar disturbances originate, and what are the forces brought into play which can affect our atmosphere in such varied ways? These are the questions which we try to answer in our study of solar-terrestrial relations. As happens so often in science, in the act of solving one problem we are confronted with many new ones, the solutions to which lie beyond the present frontiers of human understanding. Let us begin with some of the main facts about the sun.

THE SUN'S DISTANCE

There is a relation, discovered by Kepler, connecting the periods of revolution of the planets with their mean distances from the sun. The square of the period divided by the cube of the mean distance is constant. For any two planets, say the earth and Mars, the periods being known with high accuracy, the *ratio* of their mean distances may be obtained. Now, if the *difference* between these two lengths can also be measured in miles, the value of each will follow, and incidentally the scale of the whole solar system. Thus has arisen the paradox that, in order to obtain the sun's distance we need only measure, by trigonometrical means, the distance between the earth and any other planet near the time of its closest approach. Venus and Mars have been used for this purpose, but the minor planet Eros, being both smaller and nearer, is much more favourable. In 1931 Eros approached within 16 million miles of the earth, and from the observations which were made at that time Sir Harold Spencer Jones has since deduced the mean distance of the sun to be 93,009,000 miles, or 149,500,000 km. This measurement is believed to be correct to about 10,000 miles. The distance is such that a rocket travelling at 1,000 miles an hour would take 10·6 years to reach the sun; a ray of light takes 500 seconds, or 8·3 minutes.

The actual distance of the earth from the sun varies by nearly 3 million miles, due to the eccentricity of the earth's orbit, the distance being least when the earth is at perihelion in early January, and greatest when at aphelion in the beginning of July. From this cause alone the sun's heat and light received on earth varies by about 7 per cent in the course of the year.

DIMENSIONS, MASS AND DENSITY

As the sun's distance changes, so inversely does its apparent diameter vary as seen in the sky. The greatest and least values are 32′ 35″ and 31′ 31″, in January and July respectively. The mean value of this angle, as measured

B

5

from the earth's centre, is 31′ 59″, or 1,919″. This is also the angle subtended by a halfpenny (1 inch in diameter) at a distance of 9 feet. Now at the sun's mean distance an angle of 1″ corresponds to 450 miles, or 725 km.; hence, we readily obtain for the sun's diameter 864,000 miles, or 1,390,000 km. Unlike the earth, whose equatorial diameter is 0·34 per cent greater than its polar diameter, the globe of the sun is not measurably flattened by its slower rotation on its axis. A point on the sun's equator rotates in 25 days relative to the stars and in 27 days relative to the earth.

The mass of the sun in terms of the earth's mass has been found by an application of Newton's law of gravitation. When this calculation is performed (see Appendix 1) we find that the sun contains approximately 332,000 times the amount of matter in the earth. This result also enables us to compare the mean densities of the two bodies; for density is mass divided by volume, and the sun's volume is $(109)^3$ times that of the earth, 109 being the ratio of the two radii. Consequently the sun's mean density is $332,000/(109)^3 = 0·256$ that of the earth. Bearing in mind that the mean density of the earth is 5·52 compared with water, that of the sun will be 5·52 × 0·256, or 1·4 times the density of water.

Let us compare the weight of this book with its weight on the sun. Provided we neglect small effects due to centrifugal force, the weight a body would have on another planet is directly proportional to the mass of the attracting planet and inversely proportional to the square of its radius. The sun's mass, as we have seen, is 332,000 times the earth's mass and its radius is 109 times the earth's radius. Hence the pull of gravity on the sun will be $322,000/109^2$, or 28 times that on the earth. If the book weighs 1 lb. on the earth it will weigh 28 lb. on the sun.

These two results—the low mean density combined

with the enormous pull of gravity—are of the greatest importance to our understanding of what goes on inside the sun. We know from the evidence of the spectroscope that the sun's matter is made up very largely of the same chemical elements we find on the earth, and the only way in which we can reconcile these facts is to assume that the temperature inside the sun is so high that solids and liquids cannot exist—the sun in fact is a glowing ball of gas.

SOLAR LEVELS

Even though the sun is entirely gaseous and can have no solid or liquid surface like the planets, it is far from being featureless. Indeed, the outer layers which are accessible to observation are stratified into many different levels, each showing characteristic and ever-changing types of activity. Let us go on a brief tour of inspection.

We may as well start in the central regions (Fig. 1.1) which we now know to be the great power house, not merely of the sun itself, but of the whole solar system. Through the brilliant researches begun many years ago by Sir Arthur Eddington and through the work of the nuclear physicists a great deal is known about the conditions which must exist in this region. The temperature is of the order of 20 million degrees, a figure that may seem quite inconceivable by terrestrial standards. But after all, temperature is only a measure of the average motion of the atoms, and it means quite simply that the gas atoms here are shooting along between their collisions at speeds of about 100 miles per second, as compared with speeds of less than 1 mile per second in the air above our heads. The pressure, however, is 1,000 million times that of the air we breathe. This is the crux of the matter, for we must conclude that, despite their rapid motions, the atoms are immensely tightly packed, so much so that they bear

7

little resemblance to the atoms of ordinary air. Most of our terrestrial atoms lead a very tame existence by comparison; their nuclei are surrounded by rings of satellite

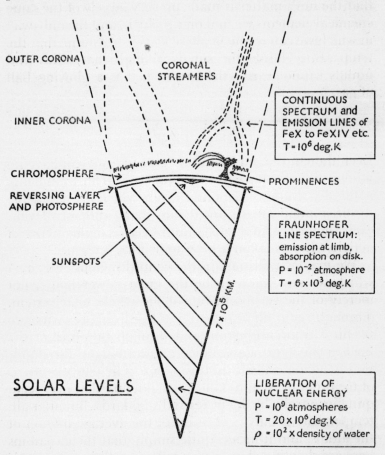

OUTER CORONA

CORONAL STREAMERS

INNER CORONA

CONTINUOUS SPECTRUM and EMISSION LINES of FeX to FeXIV etc.
$T = 10^6$ deg. K

CHROMOSPHERE

PROMINENCES

REVERSING LAYER AND PHOTOSPHERE

FRAUNHOFER LINE SPECTRUM:
emission at limb, absorption on disk.
$P = 10^{-2}$ atmosphere
$T = 6 \times 10^3$ deg. K

SUNSPOTS

7×10^5 KM.

SOLAR LEVELS

LIBERATION OF NUCLEAR ENERGY
$P = 10^9$ atmospheres
$T = 20 \times 10^6$ deg. K
$\rho = 10^2 \times$ density of water

FIG. 1.1.—A section of the sun and its atmosphere. In this diagram the depths of chromosphere and reversing layer are considerably exaggerated.

electrons, each one carrying a negative charge, and sufficient in number to balance the number of positive charges upon the central nucleus. When an atom is maltreated, by impact or by absorption of short-wave radiation, it may lose one or more of its planetary electrons and it is then said to be ionized. In the atomic squash and jostle near the centre of the sun these crinolines of outer electrons are largely swept away, so that many more atoms can be accommodated within the same space. Indeed, the packing is so close that the density of matter here is some hundred times that of water, or say five times the density of platinum. In addition to these ionized atoms there are, of course, vast numbers of free electrons darting about at even greater speeds. There is also an abundance of light; but the light is not of a kind with which we are very familiar. The light photons carry so much energy that we should call them X-rays or γ-rays.

As we shall see later, all this energy is derived from the slow conversion of matter into radiation. Every now and then two of these atomic nuclei, which have been shorn of their protecting electron shells, will make a head-on collision, and in the subsequent rearrangement of the nuclear particles a small fraction of their mass may be converted into the energy of γ-radiation. These thermo-nuclear reactions, as they are called, take place in a completely controlled manner, and not explosively as in an atomic bomb. At all levels inside the sun there is a delicate equilibrium between the opposing forces of gravity pulling inwards and the pressure of radiation streaming outwards. If the rate of energy production were to increase, the result would merely be a slight expansion of the outer layers. This, in turn, would lead to cooling and slowing down of the atoms, and the liberation of energy would drop back again to its original value.

Proceeding outwards through the solar gases we notice that there is little movement of the atoms and electrons as a whole; they continue to jostle one another about, though at decreasing speeds, and appear to get nowhere. The γ-ray photons, however, do succeed in making some progress in an outward direction. After countless absorptions and re-emissions by atoms their energies gradually become less and their wavelengths increase. At one level we shall recognize them as X-rays, at another as ultra-violet light, and so on, until, as we are nearing the sun's surface, the most common wavelengths observed will be those of visible light.

THE PHOTOSPHERE

By this time we are at a level nearly 700,000 km. (430,000 miles) from the sun's centre, and quite suddenly we become aware of the outside world; stars and planets begin to be visible. This region, where the solar gases thin out into transparency, is called the photosphere. Conversely, when we look down into the sun from the earth, the photosphere is the deepest layer to which our vision can penetrate.

The photosphere is the most important solar level, in the sense that we receive from it the greater part of our light and heat, and, indeed, this is the origin of its name —the 'light'-sphere. The density here is less than one-thousandth part of atmospheric air and the temperature is in the region of 6,000° K.[1] 10380°F

The light emitted by the photosphere is similar in quality to that received from any other very hot body, say the filament of an electric light bulb. It has a continuous emission spectrum, all visible wavelengths being represented, and there are no gaps in the spectrum. The photosphere is an extremely thin layer, perhaps no more than 100 or 200 km. deep, and it is this fact which gives to the sun its perfectly sharp outline, similar to that of a

[1] Degrees Kelvin, i.e. temperature measured from the absolute zero, or Centigrade + 273°.

solid surface. The reason lies in the rapid decrease of pressure with height, which arises from the great pull of gravity upon the solar gases.

Before we leave the photosphere we should notice that this is the level at which sunspots occur. These are vast disturbances, perhaps cyclonic in character, which, by their number and size, indicate most clearly the state of the sun's activity. The number of sunspots varies in an approximately cyclical manner with an average period of 11 years. The largest sunspots are visible to the unaided eye, and have been so recorded since the second century A.D.

THE SOLAR ATMOSPHERE

The levels above the photosphere may be regarded as the solar atmosphere. As we rise above the photosphere we first pass through a stratum of cooler gas, about 1,000 km. (620 miles) deep, known as the *reversing layer*. In this region many of the atoms are either electrically neutral, which means that their shells of planetary electrons are intact, or at most they have lost only one electron, in which case we say they are singly ionized. Under these relatively quiescent conditions an atom can absorb photons of visible light which have just the right energy to raise one of the planetary electrons from its normal orbit round the nucleus of the atom to outer orbits having higher energies. After resting in this excited state for a period of about 100 millionth of a second the atom unloads the extra energy, either in a single electron jump back to the original level, or in a series of jumps. Moreover, the direction of the emitted photon may be quite different from that in which it was travelling before it was absorbed. The net result of these processes is the formation of narrow depressions, or absorption lines, in the continuous spectrum of the light coming through

from the photosphere. These are known as the Fraunhofer lines (Plate II). They were first observed by Wol-
laston in 1802, and in 1816 they were studied in greater
detail by Fraunhofer, the celebrated optician of Münich.

More than 20,000 absorption lines have been mapped
out in the solar spectrum. Not all of them originate in the
reversing layer; some are formed at higher levels, and
still others are produced by molecules of oxygen and
water-vapour in our own atmosphere. By ingenious
methods the solar physicists have been able to sort them
out, and by measurements of their wavelengths, breadths
and intensities they have learnt to unravel the chemical
and physical secrets of the sun's atmosphere.

THE CHROMOSPHERE

The reversing layer merges without any sharp boundary
into the chromosphere, or 'colour' sphere. During the
brief moments of a total eclipse, when the intense light of
the photosphere is blotted out by the passage of the
moon's disk, the chromosphere appears as a ring of red
light surrounding the sun. It owes its characteristic colour
to hydrogen, one of its chief constituents. This gas has its
strongest visible spectral line, the $H\alpha$ line, in the red at
a wavelength of 6,563 A.[1] When the spectra of the
chromosphere and reversing layer are photographed at
such times they are found to consist entirely of emission
lines at discrete wavelengths, an indication that we are
dealing with a hot gas at low pressure The wavelengths
of the emission lines tell us that, for the most part, they
are formed by the same atoms as those which give rise to
the Fraunhofer spectrum. The eclipse spectra also show
that the $H\alpha$ line of hydrogen fades out at a height of about

[1] A. stands for angstroms—the unit of length (10^{-8} cm.) in which wavelengths are measured. The visible spectrum extends approximately from
4,000 A. to 7,000 A.

12,000 km. (7,500 miles) above the photosphere, and the highest lines of all, the H and K lines of ionized calcium, cease to be visible at a height of 14,000 km. (8,700 miles). This level is, therefore, regarded as the top of the chromosphere. A temperature of 30,000° K. for the chromosphere was obtained by Redman, but this high value is regarded as somewhat uncertain.

The chromosphere may now be observed at all times by means of such instruments as the spectrohelioscope and spectroheliograph, to be described later.

THE CORONA

The extended outer atmosphere of the sun lying beyond the chromosphere is known as the corona. The light of the corona is so feeble, being comparable in total brightness to the light of the full moon, that it can only be seen in its entirety during a total eclipse (Plate V). On these occasions its appearance is that of a beautiful halo of white light, standing out in wonderful contrast to the red colour of the chromosphere and prominences, and here and there extending far into space, in the form of faint petals and streamers, to distances of many solar diameters. Lyot's instrument, the coronagraph, now enables us to observe the bright inner corona from mountain stations in clear weather without waiting for an eclipse. Many lines of evidence show that the coronal temperature is in the region of 1,000,000° K.

PROMINENCES

These are unlike any of the other features we have mentioned; for they are not confined to any one level, but extend vertically through both chromosphere and corona. They are glowing clouds of vapour, the light from which is composed mainly of the emission lines of hydrogen, helium and ionized calcium. In these characteristic wavelengths they are sufficiently bright to be seen at any time with a simple spectroscope or with other types of monochromatic filter. Prominences have many different forms, all of which exhibit complex internal structure and remarkable movements. From the widths of their spectral lines Mrs. H. A. Brück has deduced that the temperatures of prominences range between 10,000 and 20,000° K.

THE SUN'S COLOUR AND TEMPERATURE

We have seen that the photosphere is a thin layer of hot gas which emits nearly all the heat and light that we receive on earth. Much painstaking work has been carried out in order to determine the spectral composition of this light, or, in simple language, to determine its colour.

As the temperature of any heated body rises it first emits a dull red glow; this changes slowly towards 'white' heat, and eventually it becomes 'blue' hot. The shapes of the spectral energy curves have been obtained by measurements in the laboratory for low-temperature sources, and they may be calculated for any higher temperature by means of Planck's radiation law (see Appendix 2). In Fig. 1.3 we see three of these colour curves which have been plotted (full lines) for temperatures of 5,000°, 6,000° and 7,000° K. Such curves apply only to the energy emitted by *perfect radiators*. The nearest approach to a perfect radiator obtainable in the laboratory is provided by an enclosure at *uniform temperature*, the radiation being studied through a small aperture in the side of the enclosure. The intensity of radiation of given wavelength from such an enclosure depends upon the temperature and on nothing else. Perfect radiators are also perfect absorbers of radiation; since they reflect no light and would appear absolutely black when cold they are sometimes called 'black bodies'. We also notice from Fig. 1.3

that the wavelength of maximum energy output becomes shorter and shorter as the temperature increases (Wien's Law).

Thus, in principle, all that is needed to find the temperature of the solar surface is a knowledge of the intensity distribution of the light in different wavelengths of the continuous spectrum radiated from the photosphere. We can then ascertain for what temperature the observed curve makes the best fit with the theoretical curve.

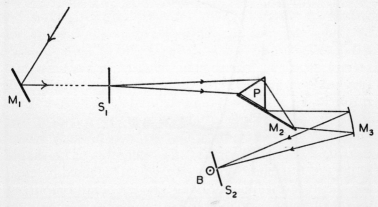

FIG. 1.2.—Apparatus for measuring the energy distribution within the sun's spectrum—Langley's spectrobolometer.

Temperatures so deduced are referred to as 'colour temperatures'.

In practice these measurements are immensely difficult, because of the uncertain losses sustained by the radiation as it traverses the earth's atmosphere and then the recording instruments. The measuring apparatus, as used by Langley and later investigators, is shown in Fig. 1.2. M_1 is a siderostat mirror driven by clockwork so as to maintain a beam of sunlight directed on to the slit (S_1) of a spectrograph; the prism P, made of rock-salt, disperses the light into its colours and the spectrum is focused by the mirrors M_2 and M_3 on to the selecting slit (S_2).

Behind S_2 is placed a delicate bolometer (B) which transforms the radiant energy into an electric current so that it may be measured by means of a galvanometer. As the

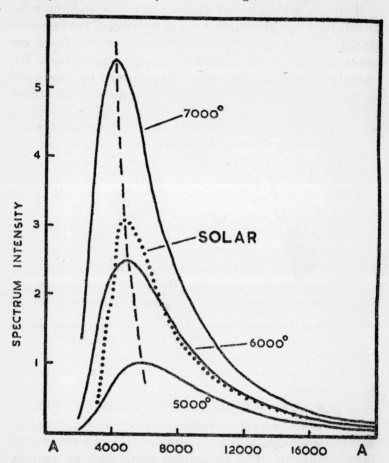

FIG. 1.3.—Energy distribution within the solar spectrum (sun's colour) compared with that of perfect radiators at 5,000°, 6,000°, and 7,000° K.

mirror M_2 is rotated, different parts of the spectrum are made to pass across the slit. Corrections are then applied, first for the energy absorbed by the optical parts of the

16

spectrograph, and secondly by transmission through the atmosphere. These losses are different in each wavelength and they also depend upon the length of the atmospheric path.

When all these corrections have been made one obtains the spectral energy curve for sunlight received from the whole disk, as shown by the dotted line in Fig. 1.3. It is only too clear that it is not a particularly good fit for any of the 'black body' curves. In the wavelengths of the infra-red (from 7,500 A. upwards) it runs fairly close to the theoretical curve for a temperature of 6,000° K., but rises above this in the visible region of the spectrum and falls below it in the ultra-violet. Thus the intensities of individual wavelengths indicate different temperatures, and it is usual to take the round number of 6,000° K. as the sun's effective temperature.

There are several reasons why the energy radiated from the photosphere is not distributed precisely like that from a perfect radiator. In the first place its temperature is not constant, but increases with depth, and light of different wavelengths will originate in different levels. Secondly, there is considerable convection and turbulence in the photosphere, so that its temperature may be expected to vary horizontally as well as vertically.

THE SOLAR CONSTANT

Bottled sunshine in one form or another—coal, oil, wind, water-power and so on—provides the only source of power which is readily available to us. Let us consider just how much radiant energy is being supplied for heating the earth and for storage in these ways.

The solar constant is defined as being the *total radiation energy* (included in all wavelengths and from the whole of the sun's disk) received vertically on 1 square centimetre in 1 minute, the receiver being just outside the earth's atmosphere and the sun being at its mean distance. Whereas Langley's spectral energy curve gives us the energy received wavelength by wavelength, the solar constant provides a measure of the total energy obtained from the addition of all wavelengths in the spectrum. The area under the spectral energy curve, therefore, represents the value of the solar constant.

In practice the value of the constant is derived from measures made with a pyrheliometer, consisting essentially of a blackened metal disk exposed to the sun's rays. The energy, being transformed into heat, is measured by observing the rise in temperature of a stream of water which flows in contact with the heated back of the disk. Dr. Abbot and his collaborators of the Smithsonian Institution have used these instruments on mountain tops in many parts of the world and over a long period of years. Owing to the great uncertainty of the corrections to be applied, especially for the very short and very long waves which do not penetrate the atmosphere, the value of the solar constant, which is now taken as close to 2·0 calories per square centimetre per minute, may still be in error by some 5 per cent.

The figures in Table I illustrate the way in which the solar energy at different wavelengths is depleted by its passage through the terrestrial atmosphere. If the incident radiation is represented by 100 for each wavelength, the figures show the percentages which penetrate down to heights of 14,500 ft. and sea-level respectively.

TABLE I

Wavelength (A.)	2900	3000	4000	5000	6000	8000	10000
Percentage received at 14,500 ft.	0	55	81	92	94	98	97
Percentage received at sea-level	0	0	56	73	78	89	92

One observes that the short waves are relatively much weaker at sea-level than at high altitudes. This fact may become painfully obvious when climbing in the Alps; for the wavelengths mainly responsible for sunburn are those in the 3,000–4,000 angstrom band, and these may often be twice as intense on a mountain top as at sea-level. At the other end of the spectrum the variation with height is inappreciable.

The value of the solar constant indicates that at the top of the atmosphere radiant energy is being received at a rate of $1·39 \times 10^6$ ergs per second on every square centimetre facing the sun. This is equivalent to saying that the sun is working for us at a rate of 1·56 horsepower over each square yard, or at the rate of 5×10^6 horsepower per square mile. Not more than 70 per cent of the total reaches us at ground level, but this would be far more than sufficient for our power needs if we had the means of harnessing it efficiently.

Armed with these figures we can now work back to find out how much radiant energy escapes from the solar surface in one second. The value is about 1,540 calories per square centimetre per second, being equivalent to a rate of working of 72,000 horsepower per square yard. Another of the radiation laws—that of Stefan-Boltzmann —enables us to say just how hot a body must be for its surface to radiate at this rate. The temperature is 5,790° K. We call this the sun's radiation temperature, and it is satisfactory to find that it comes out in reasonable agreement with the colour temperature of 6,000° K.

LIMB DARKENING

The solar hemisphere presented to us does not appear uniformly bright. When we project an image of the sun several feet in diameter on to a white wall in a darkened room it is at once obvious that the regions near the limb are both *dimmer and redder* than the centre of the disk. This effect, known as limb darkening, arises from the circumstance that when we look towards the edge of the sun our line of vision penetrates the solar atmosphere at a large angle with the vertical. Near the centre of the disk we can see in to deeper levels, and the deeper we go in the photosphere the hotter it becomes. Consequently, the radiation from the centre of the disk originates in lower strata and has a higher effective temperature than that which reaches us from the near limb. The reduction in brightness towards the limb is greatest in the shortest wavelengths.

CONSTANCY OF SOLAR RADIATION

Having defined what we mean by the solar constant, we immediately proceed to ask: does it vary? Such a question exposes the inadequacy of our nomenclature, but it is also very relevant, for this reason. The sun is an average star, and many of the stars show large, periodic fluctuations in their light. The sun's activity also—as measured by the frequency of sunspots and in many other ways—exhibits a regular cycle of period about 11 years. May there not occur corresponding variations in the solar output of light and heat?

This question admits of no simple answer. While the absolute value of the solar constant is still uncertain within about 5 per cent, relative measures made from one observing station are more accurate than this, and it is reasonable to suppose that real variations of as little as 1 per cent, if they existed, could be measured. Records were made daily for a number of years at three mountain stations far apart—Brukkaros in South West Africa, Table Mountain in California and Montezuma in Chile. Occasionally, irregular variations were found, lasting for a year or more and affecting all three stations at about the same time. These changes were no greater than 1 per cent, and their origin—in the sun or in the earth's atmosphere—is still subject to controversy.

An alternative method of enquiry is to compare the brightness of the sun with that of another star known to be constant. Here we face the difficulty that the sun is 10,000 million times brighter than the brightest star—Sirius—and direct comparison becomes impossible. However, the planets shine by reflected sunlight; and the mean brightness of a planet will depend upon that of the sun. It is a fairly easy matter to compare the brightness of Jupiter or Uranus with that of some standard star in the same region of the sky. Allowance must be made for the variability in the distances of the planet from the sun and from the earth. Such measures, carried out photoelectrically by Stebbins and others, all lead to the same conclusion; namely, the sun's radiation does not vary by more than 1 per cent in the visible region of the spectrum, whether there are many sunspots or few sunspots.

Now, these conclusions are in striking contrast to what we know about the variability of the sun's output of ultra-violet light. In 1939, Appleton and Naismith were able to show, by means of radio measurements made in connection with the ionosphere, that the solar ultra-violet radiations, which are responsible for the formation and maintenance of the ionized layers of the atmosphere, had increased by a factor of two between the years of sunspot minimum (1933) and sunspot maximum (1937). As we shall see later, this discovery has been verified by subsequent work and has become of the greatest practical importance in relation to the problems of transmitting radio waves round the world. Similar large variations, related to the 11-year sunspot cycle, have been found to occur in the intensity of the short radio waves emitted by the sun.

Thus it appears that, while the radiation in the visible

C

region is nearly constant, at the two extremes—in the ultra-violet and in the radio bands [1]—the sun must be regarded as a *variable star* whose period is 11 years.

THE SOURCE OF THE SUN'S ENERGY

We have seen that the sun is delivering heat and light freely and steadily into space at a rate of 72,000 horse-power from every square yard of its surface. This is equivalent to a rate of $5 \cdot 1 \times 10^{23}$ horsepower, or $3 \cdot 8 \times 10^{23}$ kilowatts, from the whole solar surface.

One hundred years ago William Thomson (later Lord Kelvin) began to enquire what was the source which maintained and replenished this vast liberation of energy. If the sun were merely using up its original store of heat, without replenishment, it was easy to demonstrate that its temperature would fall by about 2 degrees per year. Clearly, on this basis, its lifetime could not exceed more than a few thousand years; even the most energetic chemical reactions taking place inside could not prolong its life sufficiently. Kelvin concluded that the energy must be derived from meteors falling into the sun under the action of its gravitational attraction. Some years later, however, he felt compelled to abandon this idea, and substituted for it the view, which had been proposed by Helmholtz, that the sun was slowly shrinking, and in so doing was converting its gravitational store of energy into heat. On the earth, for example, the temperature at the bottom of a waterfall is greater than at the top, because the energy supplied to the torrent by gravity has appeared as heat. Kelvin and his great contemporary, Joule, had verified this fact for themselves in 1847, when they carried a thermometer with them on their tour of Switzerland.

[1] Of course, neither of these wave-bands contributes more than a minute fraction to the total energy of solar radiation.

By simple calculations Kelvin was able to prove that the enormous gravitational pull of the sun combined with a slow rate of contraction would supply all the heat that was needed. But even this source would become exhausted at the present rate of expenditure in about 20 million years. The geologists could not accept so short a time-scale as this; it appeared to them nothing like sufficient to embrace the whole pageant of creation, as revealed by the rocks and the fossils. About fifty years ago the discovery of radioactivity began to give much more precision to the geological estimates for the age of the earth's crust. Rayleigh and Joly, by measurements made upon uranium, thorium and their disintegration products in the rocks, were led to values of 1,000 million years for the ages of the oldest strata. More recently, these methods have been greatly refined by Holmes, who arrives at a figure of some 3,300 million years for the full age of the earth.

The sun's age cannot well be less that this. Therefore, we may suppose it has been radiating energy at something like its present rate for close on 4,000 million years. If this is so, it follows that each pound of the sun's matter must already have yielded up about 10^{20} ergs, or say 3 million kilowatt-hour units of energy. Put in another way, the energy from 1 lb. of solar matter would be sufficient to keep an average domestic electric fire burning for 3 million hours!

As we know to our cost, the complete combustion of 1 lb. of coal provides us with almost exactly one millionth part as much heat. In other words the sun can tap stores of energy one million times greater per pound of matter than those which are available to us in the form of ordinary chemical reactions.

This was the situation as Eddington saw it about 1925. He then drew the fairly obvious conclusion that sub-atomic, or as we now say nuclear, energy was being released in the deep interiors of the sun and the stars. No other explanation could fit the facts. At that time two possible ways were being suggested by which the nuclear energy might be released. First, Einstein in 1905 had proposed the equivalence of mass and energy; m grams of matter were equivalent to mc^2 ergs of energy, c being the velocity of light, that is 3×10^{10} cm./sec. One gram of matter completely converted would, therefore, yield 9×10^{20} ergs. It was known that four hydrogen atoms made one helium atom. Taking the mass of a hydrogen atom to be 1, the mass of the helium atom should have been exactly 4. But it was not. The mass of helium was found to be 3·97, and it was supposed that the extra 0·03 grams had been converted into energy during the building up of the helium atoms from hydrogen. This process of atom building, if it could take place quietly and steadily in the centre of a star, would yield the necessary energy supply.

Sir James Jeans, on the other hand, preferred the idea of the annihilation of matter. He supposed that under certain conditions positive and negative charges rushing together might completely annihilate one another and thus set free their whole mass as radiation. At the time, the helium building process seemed to imply the occurrence of a very unlikely event, namely the coming together in a simultaneous collision of four hydrogen protons to form one helium nucleus. But obviously, since helium existed, this must have happened some time and somewhere; so why not *now* in the centre of a star? The annihilation of matter, in the form proposed by Jeans, was a pure hypothesis for which there was no observational evidence; and in any case it yielded too large an energy supply and, therefore, indicated too great an age for the stars.

During the next fifteen years the rapid advance of nuclear physics provided definite answers to these speculations. It was in the year 1919 that the first nitrogen nucleus was broken up by Rutherford, using the naturally occurring α-particles of Radium C as his bombarding projectiles. The energy possessed by the α-particles was several million electron-volts,[1] but the chances of achieving head-on collisions with the atomic nuclei were exceedingly small. If α-particles or hydrogen protons could be accelerated in a discharge tube between electrodes having a similar potential difference, nuclear reactions might be brought about artificially on a much larger scale. It would no longer be necessary to rely upon naturally occurring radioactive materials. However, the practical difficulties were too great to be surmounted by the physicists and engineers at the time. It was in 1928 that Gamow put forward a simple interpretation of radioactivity, based upon the new wave-mechanical views of matter. This implied that not only could particles escape spontaneously from the nucleus as in radioactive disintegrations, but that a bombarding projectile of comparatively low energy approaching the nucleus from outside might get inside and shiver it to pieces. Cockcroft and Walton thus had reason to hope that artificially accelerated protons of quite moderate energies might be made to disintegrate atoms of low atomic weight; and this expectation was sensationally confirmed by those two workers at the Cavendish Laboratory in 1932, when they showed that lithium was converted into helium by bombardment with hydrogen protons of about 100,000 electron-volts energy, in accordance with the equation:

$$_3\text{Li}^7 + {}_1\text{H}^1 \rightarrow {}_2\text{He}^4 + {}_2\text{He}^4 + 17 \text{ million e.v.}$$

This is a reaction occurring between atomic nuclei; its relation to our ordinary chemical reactions may be seen by reference to Fig. 1.4. Here we have illustrated (*top*) a

[1] One electron-volt is the energy acquired by an electron in falling through a potential difference of 1 volt.

collision between a hydrogen atom and a lithium atom, such as might occur in the air of the room. The hydrogen nucleus consists of a single proton (a brick with a positive charge) and round this revolves one planet electron

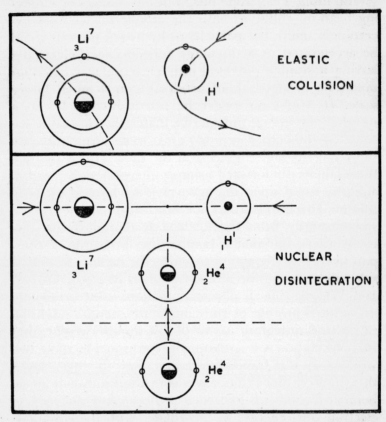

Fig. 1.4.—*Top:* Elastic collisions of atoms at low speeds, involving deflection only. *Bottom:* collisions at high speeds causing nuclear disintegration and release of energy.

which carries a negative charge. The lithium nucleus is built of seven equal bricks (three protons carrying positive charges and four neutrons without charges) and there are three planet electrons whose three negative

26

charges balance the three positive charges on the nucleus. Each nuclear brick, proton or neutron, has the same mass, but that of an electron is only one eighteen-hundredth part as great; thus virtually the whole mass of the atom is concentrated in the nucleus. When two such atoms collide at low speed the electrical forces of repulsion between the planetary electrons cause the atoms to shear away from one another long before they have made contact. At rather higher speeds the planetary systems may intermingle and hold together, a chemical compound, or molecule, being formed.

Inside the sun, as we have seen, the planetary electrons have been swept away from the atoms, collisions are more numerous and the speeds so much greater that the nuclei themselves may collide and interact. When this happens there is a rearrangement of the nuclear particles and two helium nuclei fly out in opposite directions. The important feature of this reaction is that the helium nuclei carry off with them more energy than that which was put in by the colliding particles; a small fraction of the total mass has been converted into kinetic energy. It is not thought likely that this hydrogen-lithium reaction contributes any appreciable amount of energy to the sun at present, though it may well have done so at an earlier stage of its existence when the internal temperature was in the region of 5 million degrees. Since the abundance of lithium is small this reaction must soon come to an end.

A much more efficient process for solar energy generation was discovered simultaneously in 1938 by Bethe and von Weizäcker. This is a cyclical reaction in which carbon and nitrogen atoms act as intermediaries in the conversion of hydrogen into helium but are not destroyed in the process; thus they can take part over and over again until the abundant supply of hydrogen is finally exhausted. It is now generally accepted that the carbon-nitrogen cycle is the most likely way in which nuclear mass is converted into energy in average stars of the main sequence like the sun.

THE SUN'S PLACE IN THE GALAXY

Our sun is just an average star in the Milky Way system. It is not even centrally placed in this whirling disk of 100,000 million stars. Rapid rotation has flattened out the galactic matter into a thin circular sheet about 100,000 light years in diameter and 10,000 light years thick. The sun is located some 30,000 light years from the massive central nucleus of stars, or about two-thirds the distance from the centre towards the rim.

The galaxy contains not only stars, but also gas, dust and much else, with a high degree of concentration towards the plane of rotation. For this reason visibility in the direction of the galactic plane is extremely poor. In the solar neighbourhood vision is so restricted by dust clouds that we cannot see more than perhaps one-tenth of the whole. Now, radio waves are ideally suited to the penetration of this spatial fog. Their longer wavelength and freedom from scattering enable us to 'see' the most distant parts of the galaxy. Recently McGee and Bolton in Australia, observing on a wavelength of 75 cm., have located the concentrated central nucleus of the galaxy, hitherto obscured from our view in the direction of the constellation Sagittarius. Investigations carried out in Holland by Oort, van de Hulst and Muller, using the 21-cm. line radiation from the neutral hydrogen gas in space, have enabled them to map out many of the outer spiral arms analogous to those we see in neighbouring galaxies, such as the comparable M 31 in Andromeda. And by establishing that the spiral arms are trailing they have resolved a long-standing argument among astronomers.

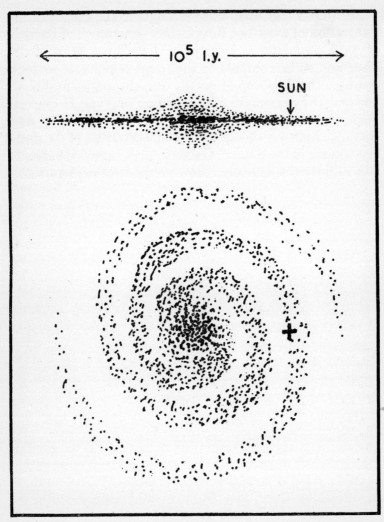

FIG. 1.5.—Location of the sun near one of the spiral arms of
the galaxy.

The sun appears to be located in, or near, one of the
spiral arms (Fig. 1.5). When we look out in the direction
of Cygnus or Vela our line of sight is directed along this

29

dusty stellar highway, and we see there the greatest concentration of those hot B-type stars—members of Baade's Type I population—believed to have been born of the dust and to be confined to the spiral regions. If we look towards the direction of the sky at right-angles to this we observe the maximum concentration of Type II objects, such as the globular clusters, planetary nebulae and novae, which are thought to be characteristic of the dust-free centre of the galaxy. Galactic 'geography' is expanding rapidly through these new methods of exploration.

CHAPTER II

The Sun's Activity

GRANULATION

E VEN when no sunspots are visible a careful examination reveals that there is much fine structure in the solar surface. When seen under the best conditions, this structure has been variously compared to the appearance of 'rice-grains', 'willow-leaves' and so on. We now speak of *granulation*, a term introduced by Father Secchi, of the Roman College Observatory. Each of these granules or nuclei is approximately circular, has a diameter of about 1,500 km. (930 miles) and a lifetime of a few minutes. Plaskett finds that the surface brightness of a granule may be as much as 10 per cent greater than that of its surroundings. As one granule subsides and fades away another develops to take its place without much lateral movement. Cinematograph films of these phenomena, such as those taken from the Pic du Midi by the late Dr. Bernard Lyot, give a vivid impression of the sun's surface being alive and 'boiling'. The granulations are believed to be the tops of convection currents which originate in unstable layers below the photosphere and which transport the sun's heat on the last lap of its journey out into space.

SUNSPOTS

Occasionally, the granulations may separate to form a small dark area between them, known as a *pore*, and when

31

several of these pores unite a sunspot is born. In the early stages of development the pores tend to cluster round two centres of activity—the *leading* and *following* spots. Since the sun rotates on its axis from east to west the leading

THE STONYHURST SUN DISCS   N.º 8.

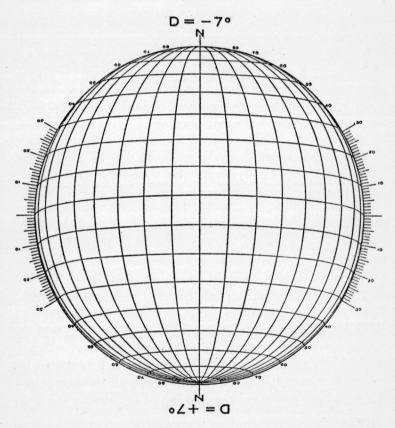

FIG. 2.1.—Stonyhurst Sun Disk, as used for determining the latitude and longitude (heliographic) of sunspots by the projection method. Eight different disks are available, corresponding to the variations in tilt from + 7° to − 7° of the N pole of the sun's axis towards or away from the earth.

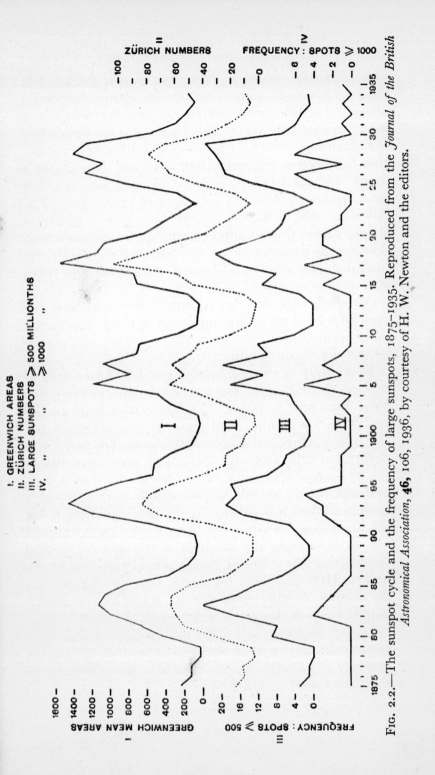

FIG. 2.2.—The sunspot cycle and the frequency of large sunspots, 1875–1935. Reproduced from the *Journal of the British Astronomical Association*, **46**, 106, 1936, by courtesy of H. W. Newton and the editors.

spot is the most westerly of the pair. During the first few days the two main spots move rapidly apart in longitude, almost as if they were repelling one another, and at the same time each grows in size. After about ten days when the maximum areas have been reached the rate of separation has become negligible: the spots are then as much as $10°-15°$ apart in longitude ($1°$ of longitude, near the solar equator, is equal to a distance of $12,000$ km.). The following spot, which is usually the more irregular in shape, decays quickly after attaining its maximum size, whereas the leader, which is compact and regular in outline, dwindles slowly and has an average life four times that of its companion.

Although this may be regarded as the normal life cycle of a large sunspot group, there is much variability. Some spots last for only a few hours or days; others may be seen for many months.

Every fully developed sunspot consists of two distinct regions, the dark inner *umbra* which is surrounded by the more luminous *penumbra*. The boundaries between the umbra and penumbra, and between the penumbra and the photosphere, are surprisingly sharp (Fig. 2.3). The umbra has little structure and covers about one-fifth of the total area. The penumbra is characterized by a mass of detail, mostly too fine to photograph and too complex to draw. When it is seen under the best conditions it has the appearance of white-hot threads, or straws, combed out, as it were, in the direction of the spot centre and terminating like eaves of thatch round the edge of the umbra. Here and there the straws separate and one has the illusion of seeing down through a roof into cavernous depths beneath. Large spots are to some extent hollows in the photosphere, and it has been suggested that these penumbral 'straws' are a sectional view of the convection currents whose tops we see elsewhere projecting above the photosphere as granulation.

34

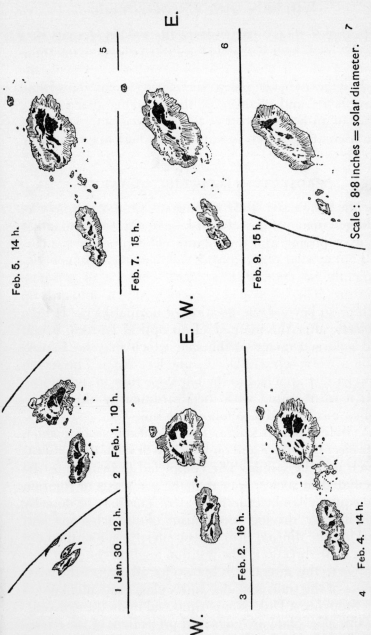

FIG. 2.3.—The passage across the solar disk of the great sunspot of 1946 February. Drawings made by the author at Sherborne, by projection with a 6-inch refractor. Reproduced from the *Journal of British Astronomical Association*, **56**, 68, 1946, by courtesy of the editors.

W.

E. W.

E.

1 Jan. 30. 12 h.   2 Feb. 1. 10 h.

3 Feb. 2. 16 h.

4 Feb. 4. 14 h.

Feb. 5. 14 h.

Feb. 7. 15 h.

5

6

Feb. 9. 15 h.

7

Scale : 8·8 inches = solar diameter.

Complex spots—particularly the following spots in a group—may have intensely luminous bridges many thousands of miles in length spanning the umbra. During the early stages of development these bridges may show rapid movements and changes of shape taking place in the space of an hour or so. For these reasons active sunspots are fascinating objects to watch under high magnification.

PROJECTION AND PHOTOGRAPHY

For the systematic study of sunspots we must project an enlarged image of the solar disk upon a screen, and either draw or photograph the picture. This procedure is carried out at solar observatories each fine day. It may conveniently be done with a small telescope of 4–6-inch aperture. The telescope eye-piece is drawn outwards an inch or so beyond the position of normal focus. It then projects, after the manner of an optical lantern, a real and enlarged image of the sun, which may be focused upon a white screen placed some feet away. The screen is preferably attached to the telescope tube in such a way that it turns round with the instrument as this is controlled mechanically to follow the sun.

A circle of 6 inches diameter is a suitable size on which to project the image and on which to draw in the sunspots which may be visible. The completed drawing must be orientated in such a way that the sun's axis of rotation and equator can be exactly located. This may be done by stopping the driving mechanism of the telescope and marking the diurnal drift of any sunspot across the field in an E–W direction. The position angle of the solar axis relative to this direction is known for all days of the year. A note of the time is made, and a glass graticule, known as a Stonyhurst Disk, is superimposed upon the drawing. On this glass plate are engraved projections of the circles of latitude and longitude (see Fig. 2.1), from which the solar, or heliographic, latitude and longitude of any sun-spot may be estimated.

If a photograph is required a plate or film must be substituted for the drawing paper; the tube should then be enclosed to exclude all extraneous light, and an expos-ing shutter incorporated to provide exposure times of about one thousandth of a second. Although a photo-graph provides a more accurate record, for many pur-poses the disk drawing is sufficiently precise, and it is available at the time when it is required, rather than a day later! This means of projecting the features of the sun's surface has been in use with simple modifications since the days of Fabricius, Galileo and Father Scheiner, all of whom began to observe sunspots telescopically during the years of 1610–11.

NUMBER, AREA AND PERIODICITY OF SUNSPOTS

The number of sunspots varies from day to day and from year to year; the number counted also depends to some extent upon the observer and his telescope. Wolf, of the Zürich Observatory, introduced the term 'relative sun-spot number' as a measure of solar activity based upon sunspot counts. The sunspot number (R) is expressed by the formula

$$R = k(10g + f),$$

where g is the number of disturbed regions (groups plus isolated spots) and f is the total number of spots, whether in groups or not. The constant k has a value depending upon the instrument used, which must be derived by experience at each observatory. For observations made at Zürich, with a telescope of aperture 8 cm. and magni-fying power 64, k has the value 1. The results from many observatories are collected and examined at Zürich, where the final sunspot number is compiled for each day.

This may seem to be a rather arbitrary procedure for the measurement of solar activity; and, indeed, it does not give sufficient importance to the large, active sunspot groups, which, as we shall see, are of great importance in the study of solar-terrestrial relations. The measurement of the total area of sunspots from daily photographs, as is carried out by the Royal Greenwich Observatory at Herstmonceux, is a better system, but even this method cannot distinguish between two sunspot groups of equal size, one of which, as often happens, is active and the other quiescent.

However, as a general index of sunspot activity, both systems are in reasonable accord, as can be seen from Fig. 2.2, which is reproduced by courtesy of H. W. Newton. In this diagram are plotted side by side the Greenwich mean areas of sunspots (I) and the Zürich relative numbers (II) from 1875 to 1935. When we are only concerned with the monthly or yearly averages both graphs correspond closely. Altogether, 18 complete cycles of activity have been studied by means of the sunspot numbers from 1749 to the present day.[1] The mean period between one maximum and the next is 11·1 years, though some periods have been as short as 7 and others as long as 17 years. The highest sunspot number reached at maximum also shows great variability. Thus, the outstanding maxima in the years 1870 and 1947 had sunspot number values three times greater than that of the lowest maximum of 1816. Waldmeier believes that these facts indicate a series of 'explosive' outbursts, following one upon the next, rather than a true repetitive cycle of activity. He has also shown that the higher the sunspot number at maximum the shorter is the time taken to reach it from the previous minimum and the longer is the subsequent decline to the next minimum. Because of these

[1] The sunspot cycle (1760–1880) is illustrated in Fig. 7.2 (p. 169), and the sunspot numbers (1750–1953) are given in Appendix 3.

irregularities little success has attended the many efforts
to predict the course of the spot cycle for more than a few
years in advance.

In Fig. 2.2 are also plotted the frequencies of occurrence of the larger sunspots observed in each cycle, i.e.
those having measured areas equal to, or greater than,
500 millionths of the sun's hemisphere (III) and those
equal to, or greater than, 1,000 millionths (IV). These
two graphs have a special interest by virtue of the fact
that a sunspot having an area of 500 millionths or more
is usually visible to the naked eye, provided that it is not
too far from the centre of the sun's disk. It follows that
any assiduous observer, using nothing more than a piece
of dark glass to reduce the sun's light, could have established the existence of the sunspot cycle had he kept continuous records of these appearances. Such observations
were occasionally made in the days before telescopes,
when the sun was dimmed by haze or fog, and some
of these are referred to in the *Chinese Annals*. Mr. S.
Hirayama, of the Tokyo Observatory, has listed 95
records of naked-eye sunspots extending over the period
A.D. 188 to 1638. But so slow was the growth of scientific
enquiry that the existence of the sunspot cycle was finally
established only in 1851, when Schwabe, of Dessau, published the results of his sunspot counts covering a period
of 25 years.

SOME GREAT SUNSPOT GROUPS

In Table II particulars are given of the half-dozen largest
sunspots which have been recorded since photographic
measurements were begun at Greenwich in 1874. The
first five in order of size occurred during the recent cycle
which culminated in May 1947. This is a clear indication
of the exceptionally high level of solar activity experienced during the past decade—the most active sunspot

period at least since 1870. In later chapters reference will be made to the remarkable terrestrial effects generated by the activity of some of these great spots.

TABLE II

*The Six Largest Sunspot Groups (1874–1954)** *

	Year	Date of C.M.P.	Max. area (millionths of sun's hemisphere)	Max. area (millions of square miles)	Latitude
1	1947	April 7	6100	7100	− 24°
2	1946	Feb. 6	5200	6100	+ 26
3	1951	May 16	4900	5700	+ 13
4	1946	July 27	4700	5500	+ 22
5	1947	Mar. 10	4600	5400	− 23
6	1926	Jan. 25	3700	4300	+ 21

* Data reproduced by kind permission of the Astronomer Royal and H. W. Newton.

Fig. 2.3 shows a series of drawings to scale of the second of these groups, as it passed across the sun's disk from its first appearance on the east limb on 1946 January 30 until its approach to the west limb on February 9. Changes in size and structure can be followed from day to day. The sun's rotation (in 27 days) brought the group back into view again in March and in April much reduced in size, and the attendant disturbances in the solar atmosphere, visible in hydrogen light, continued until a new spot (No. 4) broke out in the same active region in July.

The largest spot group on record is that which crossed the sun's central meridian on 1947 April 7; its maximum area exceeded 7,000 million square miles and it extended over 26° of solar longitude. This spot had been first observed early in February and by the beginning of March it had grown to an area of 5,400 million square miles (No. 5, Table II). Having passed its maximum in April (No. 1) it declined rapidly and was not seen again after May 11. Although the spot itself was no longer

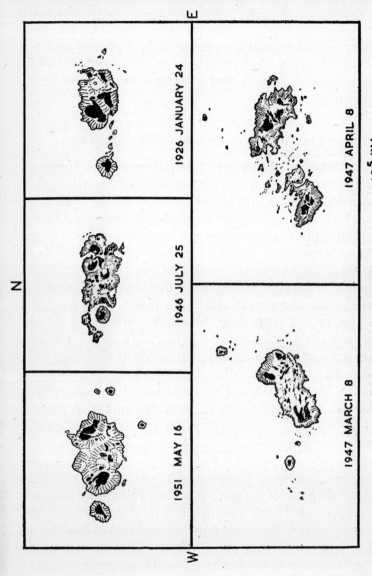

APPROXIMATE SCALE ⎯ 10⁵ KM.

Fig. 2.4.—Some famous sunspots (see Table II).

visible, the prominences generated by it were followed by means of the spectrohelioscope in successive solar rotations until September of the same year. The drawings of these great sunspots reproduced in Figs. 2.3 and 2.4 were made with a 6-inch refracting telescope, the sun's image being enlarged and projected on to a circle 18 inches in diameter.

DISTRIBUTION OF SUNSPOTS IN LATITUDE

As the number of sunspots varies through the course of the 11-year period, so the average latitude in which they occur undergoes a progressive change. At the beginning of each cycle when the spot frequency is climbing up from the minimum the new spots are located in high latitude belts centred at $\pm 30°$. As the cycle proceeds the spots appear progressively nearer and nearer to the equator; at the time of maximum frequency their average latitude is $\pm 16°$, and at the next minimum it has fallen to $\pm 8°$. For one or two years near the minimum spots of the old and new cycles may occur together. We then have sunspots appearing in four different zones at the same time —the old cycle spots in low latitudes and the new cycle spots in high latitudes. This variation of latitude, which is known as Spörer's law, is illustrated in Fig. 2.5.

THE SUN'S ROTATION PERIOD

Long-lived sunspots form useful markers from which to deduce the time of the sun's rotation. Individual sunspots may have small longitude drifts of their own, but on the average a spot near the equator is carried round and returns to its starting point after 25·0 days; in latitude $\pm 30°$ the time taken is 26·2 days. These are the true, or sidereal, rotation periods. The times taken by sunspots starting on the sun's central meridian to return again to

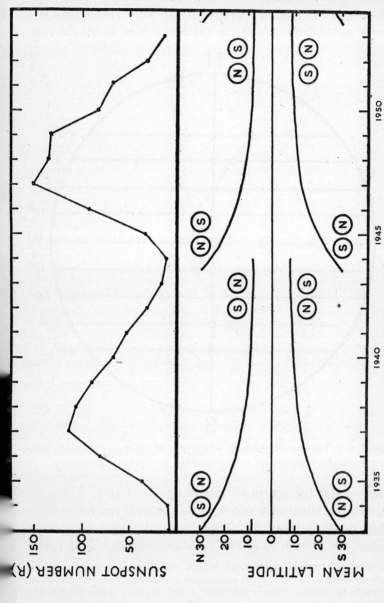

Fig. 2.5.—*Top*: Annual mean sunspot numbers, 1933–53. *Bottom*: Approximate mean latitudes of sunspots (Spörer's law). Letters within circles denote the polarities of bi-polar sunspots (sunspot polarity law), the preceding (westerly) spot being on the right.

the central meridian (as seen from the earth) are greater than this, the reason being that the solar surface rotates in the same direction as the earth revolves about the sun,

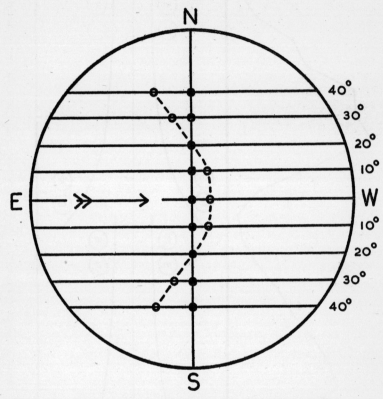

FIG. 2.6.—The movements in longitude of spots in different solar latitudes during one rotation of the sun (after Maunder).

and so the former must catch up the latter. Thus, an equatorial sunspot returns to the central meridian after 26·9 days and one in ± 30° latitude after 28·3 days. These are known as *synodic* rotation periods.[1] This varia-

[1] Many terrestrial phenomena which are dependent upon localized activity in the sun tend to recur at intervals of about 27 days. It is, therefore, useful to be able to calculate the exact synodic rotation period for different solar latitudes. The method is given in Appendix 4.

tion in the time of rotation with latitude illustrates once more that the sun is a gaseous body having no permanent surface.

Let us suppose that we have a number of long-lived sunspots lined up along the central meridian for a race round the sun, each on a different latitude track, and let us examine their relative positions one rotation later (Fig. 2.6). After 27 days the equatorial spot, being the fastest runner, will have completed its circuit and be back at the starting flag. The spots in high latitude are slower, and the further they are from the equator the more they lag behind.

Now it rarely happens that we have a line of sunspots all nicely strung out along the starting meridian so that we can watch their progress in this manner. But, as we shall see later, something of the sort does happen with the long-lived prominences. Many of these vapour clouds are generated by sunspots and spread out from them in a N–S direction. The ends of such prominences which are furthest from the equator lag behind their equatorial parts, so that after 3 or 4 months the prominence may assume the shape of a gaggle of geese flying in V-formation, the angle of the 'V' pointing in the direction of the solar rotation.

PROPERTIES OF SUNSPOTS

(1) *Faculae.*—The disturbance created by a sunspot is by no means confined to the area of the visible umbra and penumbra. Every group is surrounded by fields of faculae. These are regions where the photosphere is somewhat brighter than normal; they can be seen in white light. In the less luminous regions near the limb the faculae show up to the best advantage (see Plate I). They are believed to be regions where turbulence and convection bring up hotter gases from lower levels. They have a structure of

bright streaks, veins and irregular patches, being distributed over an area about five times that of the parent spot group. In these facular regions there occur also many other types of activity generated by the sunspot—atmospheric disturbances which can only be seen by monochromatic light, such as active sunspot prominences, flares, and excited regions in the corona. The faculae appear shortly before a sunspot is born, and endure, on the average, three times as long.

Faculae of another kind appear in the high-latitude zones, 60°–80°, near the poles. These are small, short-lived, bright flecks, 5,000–10,000 km. in diameter, which are in no way associated with sunspots. Indeed, spots are extremely rare in latitudes higher than $\pm$ 40°. The polar faculae are most frequent in the years round minimum spot activity. Father Secchi, who first observed them, believed that they were connected with those prominences which appear in high latitudes near sunspot maximum, but there is little evidence for this association.

(2) *Magnetic fields*.—The chromosphere above a sunspot frequently shows a vortex structure, when observed in hydrogen light. The chromospheric gases are largely ionized, and charged particles circulating round such a vortex might be expected to generate a magnetic field at its centre. Such ideas led Hale in 1908 to search for magnetic fields in sunspots. As Zeeman found in 1896, the single spectral lines of many elements are converted into two, or more, lines when their atoms radiate in a magnetic field. Hale's examination of the spectral lines of iron in the light from sunspots at once revealed effects of this kind.

When light is emitted in a direction parallel to the magnetic lines of force the normal spectral line is replaced by two lines equally displaced on either side of the original wavelength. The separation of the two components is proportional to the strength of the field. Moreover, the light in each line is circularly polarized with opposite directions of rotation, so that if the magnetic field is reversed the directions of their polarizations are interchanged. Consequently, when the light from a sunspot is focused upon the slit of a powerful spectrograph the intensity of the spot magnetic field can be measured from the degree of line splitting, and its type of polarity, N or S, can be distinguished. The phenomena are most easily

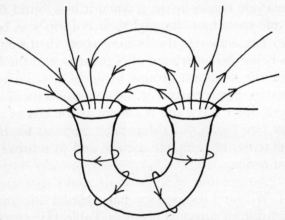

Fig. 2.7.—Hale's U-shaped vortex. Electric currents circulating in the vortex below the sun's surface are supposed to give rise to the spot magnetic field whose lines of force are shown above.

studied and interpreted when a sunspot is near the centre of the sun's disk, since the lines of force issuing from the spot are then directed approximately along the line of vision (Fig. 2.7). In a large sunspot the intensity of the field is of the order of 3,000 gauss, corresponding to a separation of about one-fifth of an angstrom between the two components of the iron line, of wavelength 6173 A., which is convenient for use in these measurements. While magnetic fields of this order can easily be generated in the laboratory by means of an electromagnet, we must remember that on the sun they may cover an area of many millions of square miles.

The majority of large sunspots are of the bi-polar type, that is to say one spot of the pair has N magnetic polarity and the other S polarity. Furthermore, Hale found that the leading spot of a bi-polar group situated north of the equator was always a S pole and the following spot always a N pole. South of the equator the polarities were in the reverse order. This state of affairs continued until the next 11-year cycle began in 1913, when it was found that the new cycle spots had changed their polarities as between the two hemispheres, the leading spots in the northern groups being henceforward of N polarity and the leading spots in the southern groups being of S polarity. This interchange has occurred at the commencement of each new cycle since 1913 and is known as the law of sunspot polarity (see Fig. 2.5). It thus takes 22 years for the sunspot polarities to complete a cycle and to return in their original order.

The examination of more than 2,000 spot groups at Mount Wilson Observatory has yielded the magnetic classification of sunspots given in Table III.

(3) *The temperature of a sunspot.*—Although the umbra of a sunspot looks black, its spectrum indicates that it is, in fact, highly luminous and that it has an effective temperature of about 4,500° K. Its darkness is simply an effect of contrast, since it is seen in proximity to the surrounding photosphere whose temperature is 6,000° K. A sunspot is therefore a refrigerating mechanism capable of maintaining a vast region of the photosphere for many weeks at a temperature more than 1,000° below that of its surroundings. How is this extraordinary condition achieved?

It seems probable that the sun's heat is carried up through the photosphere to some extent by mass motion

TABLE III

Magnetic classification	Percentage of total	Description
Unipolar (α)	14	Single spot, or small spots, of one polarity. Hydrogen and calcium plages symmetrically disposed about the group.
,, (αp)	20	Same, but centre of group precedes centre of plage.
,, (αf)	4	Same, but centre of group follows centre of plage.
Bipolar (β)	21	Two spots of opposite polarities and nearly equal in size.
,, (βp)	29	Preceding spot is the greater.
,, (βf)	8	Following spot is the greater.
,, (βγ)	3	One or other spot accompanied by smaller spots of opposite polarity.
Multipolar (γ)	1	Complex distributions of polarity.
	100	

of atoms, that is to say by convection currents, rather than by radiation which is handed on from one atom to the next, as is the case deeper down in the sun. In the granulation we see evidence of these upward currents. A sunspot, on the other hand, is a depression in the photosphere some 10,000 km. (6,200 miles) deep. In the centre of the spot the convection currents are much stronger than elsewhere and the rising gases are caused to fan outwards, probably by guidance of the ionized atoms along the lines of force of the sunspot magnetic field (Fig. 2.7). This outflow of gas, which is characteristic of every large spot, was detected by Evershed, who noticed that spectral lines in the reversing layer over the rim of the sunspot were distorted by the Doppler effect, in such a way as to indicate that the gases were flowing radially outwards over the top of the sunspot 'crater' with a speed of about

2 km./sec. directed away from its centre. The Evershed effect has since been confirmed by Abetti, Kinman and other workers. It is not known what causes a sunspot to pump gas upwards in this way, but the immediate effect is to produce cooling. Material which is rising against gravity gains potential energy and this is taken from its store of heat energy. The horizontal outflow of the gas when the photosphere is reached also transports energy from the inner to the outer regions of the spot. Both causes are believed to operate in maintaining the lowering of temperature which is observed as the darkening of the umbra and penumbra.

THEORIES OF THE 11-YEAR CYCLE

The various manifestations of the solar cycle are so re-markable and so complex that no satisfactory theory has yet been proposed to explain them. Nor is this very sur-prising when we recollect that most of our physical know-ledge has been derived from experimental work carried out under the very restricted conditions existing in terrestrial laboratories. Conditions in the sun are far re-moved from anything we can hope to imitate on the earth. We need only think of the immense scale of solar phe-nomena, of the high temperatures and low pressures in the atmosphere, of the movements of ionized gases in the presence of magnetic and electric fields, to realize that the methods of terrestrial physics are at present inade-quate to describe fully the behaviour of matter in these novel surroundings.

Recent theories of sunspots are based upon vortex ideas. They differ mainly in the methods proposed for the formation and maintenance of the solar vortices. Hale assumed that a sunspot was a U-shaped vortex of the type shown in Fig. 2.7. Suppose that the two ends of the vortex are connected below the solar surface, then those regions where it cuts the surface (the leading and following spots of a bi-polar group) will have circulations in opposite directions, one clockwise and the other counter-clockwise. If the magnetic field arises from the circulation of charged particles within the vortex the two spots will possess opposite polarities.

Bjerknes, the Norwegian meteorologist, believed that the sunspot vortices were parts of a much larger vortex, the remainder being hidden below the sun's surface. This larger vortex may be compared to a spinning smoke-ring, encircling the sun and lying in a plane parallel to the equator at no great depth below the visible surface. Disturbances of this smoke-ring would occasionally cause part of it to penetrate the surface at two neighbouring points, producing two sunspots in which the circulations would again be in opposite senses. Another smoke-ring lying below the surface in the southern hemisphere was assumed to spin in the reverse direction and to generate the southern sunspots. As the 11-year cycle progressed these two vortex rings moved slowly towards the equator until latitude $\pm 8°$ was reached at the minimum. The two rings were then supposed to contract and to sink down into the sun's interior, while two similar rings rose up to approach the surface in latitudes $\pm 30°$, and these gave rise to the new-cycle spots. The new rings were spinning in opposite directions to the former. After 22 years the original pair of smoke-rings returned to the surface in high latitudes, to begin the cycle all over again. Apart from its inherent improbability, Bjerknes' theory did offer a plausible explanation of why the latitude cycle takes place in 11 years, while the cycle of magnetic polarities occupies 22 years.

A newer and more revolutionary approach to the problem has been proposed by the Swedish physicists, Alfvén and Walén. Alfvén starts from the assumption that a strong magnetic field exists inside the sun. The shape of this field is similar to what we should expect if a bar magnet, or di-pole, were placed near the sun's centre and were aligned with its axis along the axis of rotation N–S of the sun. The solar gases are ionized and therefore electrically conducting. The problem then is to say what will happen if some of this conducting material begins to move about inside the sun, as the result, let us suppose, of convection currents occurring in the central core.

Problems concerning the flow of liquids and gases form a branch of physics known as hydrodynamics. When the material is a conductor of electricity and at the same time is flowing through a magnetic field its behaviour is totally different. A simple illustration of this will suffice. If we bring a bar magnet close to a mercury vapour, or 'sun', lamp, the path of the charged particles passing between the electrodes is so much deflected by the magnetic field that the arc may be extinguished. The study of the motion of conducting gases in the presence of magnetic fields, which Prof. Alfvén himself has done so much to develop, is known as magneto-hydrodynamics.

Let us suppose then that a small volume of conducting matter inside the sun is given a push. A conductor moving in a magnetic field generates an electromotive force; this in turn causes an electric current to flow through the material, and every flowing current possesses a magnetic field associated with it. The induced magnetism reacts with the original field in such a way as to slow down the motion. A braking action of this kind causes energy to be handed on from one part of the material to the next in the form of a wave motion. This new kind of wave, known as a magneto-hydrodynamic wave, travels out in opposite directions *along the lines of force* of the sun's field. Walén, who has developed and amplified Alfvén's ideas, has shown that these waves will assume the form of small smoke-rings (Fig. 2.8), and that when two move away simultaneously from near the sun's centre—one northwards and the other southwards—they will be spinning in opposite directions. It is estimated that it takes about 40 years for the two smoke-rings to reach the sun's surface

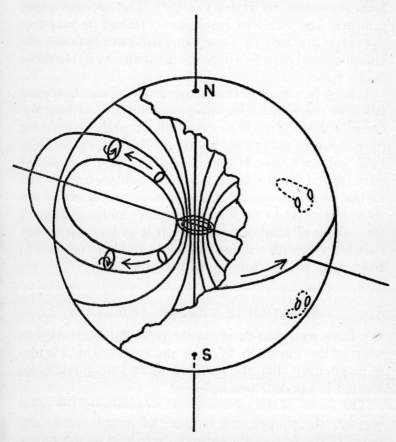

FIG. 2.8.—Smoke rings arriving at the sun's surface in Walén's theory of sunspots.

by guidance along the lines of force. Owing to the inclination of the lines of force, the rings will reach the surface earlier in high latitudes than in low latitudes.

When one of these rings intersects the surface in, say, the northern hemisphere, two sunspots will appear with

E   53

circulations in opposite directions, and the two spots will move apart in longitude until the ring has half emerged. At this stage the sunspot vortex will have exactly the form envisaged by Hale (Fig. 2.7). The corresponding group in the southern hemisphere, though it may not appear at precisely the same time, will have opposite circulations, and therefore opposite polarities, to its northern counterpart.

It must be admitted that many details of the theory are still very speculative. Its importance lies in ascribing the cause of the solar cycle to a periodic instability occurring deep down in the central regions of the sun, rather than in its surface layers. It also emphasizes the fundamental part played by the sun's magnetic field, which in the earlier 'meteorological' theories was neglected. Even though we may be far from a complete understanding of the nature of sunspot 'cyclones', it is at least clear that they are very different both in origin and in development from those we are familiar with on the earth.

MAGNETISM IN THE SUN AND STARS

We have seen that sunspots are powerful magnets; but what of the sun itself? Is there any evidence that it also is magnetized, like the earth, with two magnetic poles located in opposite hemispheres?

The forms of the solar corona, especially in the polar regions, the shapes and motions of prominences, and many of the facts of the sunspot cycle lead us to suppose that the sun is a large magnet. Some stars possess magnetic fields so intense that these are easily detected by the tell-tale Zeeman effect in their spectral lines. But when we come to measure the strength of the sun's magnetism we find that it is both weak and patchy in distribution, probably no stronger at the poles than the magnetic field of the earth, the intensity of which is approximately 1 gauss.

The sun's field, of course, can only be detected in the very thin layer of the solar atmosphere where the spectral lines are formed; nothing is known of its properties further out, or further in.

A remarkable new instrument for measuring and recording weak magnetic fields on the sun's surface has recently been developed by Babcock at the Hale Solar Laboratory in Pasadena. With this device Babcock has already shown that, whereas the solar magnetic field is fairly uniform in the polar regions, elsewhere on the sun it is highly irregular both in strength and polarity. These patches of magnetism persist for considerable periods and can be followed from day to day as the solar rotation carries them across the disk. With further study it now seems very likely that in these extensive local magnetic fields, whose strengths are no more than a few gauss as compared with the sunspot fields of several thousand gauss, we may well find the clue to the formation of the prominences and coronal streamers whose origins have hitherto remained obscure.

How do stars acquire their magnetism? And, once acquired, how is it maintained? A steel bar becomes a magnet if its atoms are given a uniform alignment, but this form of magnetization could not survive at the sun's temperature. Some people believe that stellar magnetism is a kind of 'fossil' relic of the magnetism which the stars acquire at their birth. There are facts which point to the existence of a weak magnetic field permeating the whole galaxy, a field sufficiently strong to align the metallic dust particles of space. If a large mass of this dust were to condense to form a star, the star would begin its life strongly magnetized; and such magnetism might take thousands of millions of years to die away. There are others who maintain that electric currents, flowing in the internal conducting material of a star, generate the magnetic field, in much the same way as the current in

55

a dynamo maintains the magnetism between its metal poles. Another theory, revived in recent years, postulates that all *rotating* bodies are magnetized, simply by virtue of their rotation. Just as gravitational attraction is a universal property of matter, so, it is supposed, every rotating body is endowed with its magnetic field.

None of these theories has met with general acceptance, and all are beset with great mathematical difficulties. Thus, there are, as yet, no simple answers to our questions. Notwithstanding the labours of scientists from the time of William Gilbert to the present, we cannot even explain why the earth is a magnet. This ignorance is at once a lesson in humility and a challenge to further endeavour.

CHAPTER III

The Sun's Atmosphere

OBSERVING THE CHROMOSPHERE AND PROMINENCES—THE SPECTROHELIOSCOPE

VISIBLE sunspots form only one aspect of the great centres of activity which are generated by the solar vortices. Their influence can be traced horizontally over great distances and to great heights in the sun's atmosphere. It is in these turbulent regions of the chromosphere and corona, which may persist for many months after the sunspot itself has disappeared, that we must seek the immediate causes of the phenomena which influence the earth and disturb the ionosphere. Many different instruments—ranging from optical filters to radio sets—are employed in this work; and by combining their records, gained over many years, we are slowly building up a comprehensive picture of solar-terrestrial relations.

We have seen that the chromosphere is the atmospheric layer next in order above the photosphere. It is about 14,000 km. (8,700 miles) deep and is composed mainly of hydrogen. The light which it emits is confined to discrete wavelengths, of which the lines of hydrogen (*H*α, *H*β, etc., of the Balmer series), the lines H and K of ionized calcium and the lines of neutral helium are the most important. The light emitted by atoms in the chromosphere is so feeble relative to the intense light of the photosphere that no trace of the sun's atmosphere can be seen by ordinary telescopic means. We must use

57

an instrument like the spectrohelioscope, which allows us to narrow down the range of spectral vision, so as to select just one line in the Fraunhofer spectrum and to exclude all the rest. A solar image can then be built up from the light of a single wavelength, usually the *Hα* line of hydrogen at 6563 A.

The principle of this instrument is illustrated in Fig 3·1. A plane mirror (M), aluminized on its front surface, is

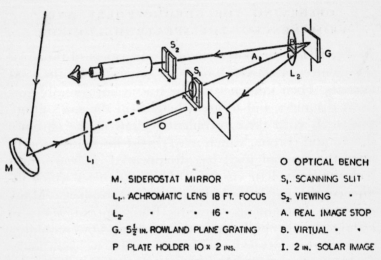

M. SIDEROSTAT MIRROR	O OPTICAL BENCH
L₁. ACHROMATIC LENS 18 FT. FOCUS	S₁. SCANNING SLIT
L₂ · · 16 · ·	S₂. VIEWING ·
G. 5½ IN. ROWLAND PLANE GRATING	A. REAL IMAGE STOP
P PLATE HOLDER 10 × 2 INS.	B. VIRTUAL · ·
	I. 2 IN. SOLAR IMAGE

FIG. 3.1.—Combined spectrohelioscope and spectrograph
(schematic).

driven by a clock mechanism so as to direct a beam of sunlight upon a lens (L₁). This lens forms an image of the sun a few inches in diameter which is focused upon the *scanning* slit (S₁), of the spectroscope. The slit allows white light from a narrow element of the image to pass through. The light is then collected by a second lens (L₂) which renders the beam parallel before it falls on the diffraction grating (G). The grating is a flat sheet of polished metal upon which some 80,000 fine parallel lines have been ruled by means of a diamond point—14,000 for every inch of its surface. The purpose of the grating is to disperse the sunlight into its constituent colours. The various colours are then returned through the same lens (L_2) and are brought to a sharp focus upon the back of the *viewing slit* (S_2), where the solar spectrum is formed. This band of spectral colours, several feet in length, is a splendid sight. It is crossed here and there by the dark Fraunhofer lines of which more than 20,000 are known (see Plate II). By a rotation of the grating the *Hα* line of hydrogen is set to fall upon this slit. Although the line looks black, it is not really so; the hydrogen light at the centre of the line is about one-seventh part as bright as the continuous spectrum near-by. Therefore, when we look through the eyepiece of the instrument, which is focused upon the slit (S_2), we see no more than a very thin strip of the sun's atmosphere glowing in the red light of hydrogen. Such an image is much too narrow to be of practical use, so we must now set the slits in oscillatory motion by means of a mechanical scanning device. The scanning slit (S_1) is caused to vibrate to and fro across the solar image at a frequency of about 20 times a second. This motion produces an oscillating spectral line at the viewing slit. The viewing slit is linked to the scanning slit so that it follows precisely the oscillations of the spectral line. Thus, at any instant, wherever the scanning slit may happen to intersect the solar image, the viewing slit transmits to the eye the hydrogen light coming from that intersection. The eye does the rest. By a very useful property, known as the persistence of vision, it builds up all these elementary slit images into a steady picture of the sun. We call this picture the monochromatic image, since it is formed by light of one colour emitted by hydrogen atoms in the chromosphere.

Plate III shows us the appearance of the chromosphere when observed in this way. We can thus study continuously, from hour to hour and from one day to the next, the turbulent motions and the changes which occur above the sunspot regions. This photograph was taken with the spectroheliograph at Meudon. There is no difference in principle between the spectrohelioscope which is used for visual observations and the spectro-heliograph which is used for photography. To obtain a photograph it is only necessary to expose a plate immediately behind the viewing slit (i.e. on the left-hand side of S_2 in Fig. 3.1); in practice, however, narrower slits and a slower speed of scanning are used for photography. The spectroheliograph was invented independently by Hale and Deslandres in 1892, and thirty years later Hale developed the first practical spectrohelioscope. Janssen had used an elementary form of the latter as early as 1869.

A most valuable feature of the spectrohelioscope is that it enables us to measure the velocity component in the line of sight of gases which are moving in the solar atmosphere. A mass of gas which is approaching us has its spectral line shifted away from the normal position towards the violet end of the spectrum; if it is receding the line is shifted towards the red. This is in consequence of the Doppler effect: when a source of light is approaching us more light waves reach us per second than if it were stationary and the frequency of the spectral line is correspondingly increased, or, what amounts to the same thing, the wavelength is diminished. The change of wavelength $(d\lambda)$, which is directly proportional to the sightline velocity (v) of the moving gases, is given by the formula $d\lambda = \lambda v/c$ where λ is the normal wavelength and c is the velocity of light. From this relation it is easy to calculate that a shift of 1 angstrom unit in the wavelength of the $H\alpha$ line represents a velocity along the line of sight of 45·7 km./sec. (28 miles/sec.). In Plate II we see a photograph of the displaced line of one of these moving hydrogen clouds. The displacement on this occasion was 3 angstroms to the violet, and so we conclude that the cloud had a sightline velocity towards us of about 140 km./sec.

These Doppler shifts are measured by means of a sheet of plane glass which is located close to the viewing slit of the spectrohelioscope, on the side next the grating. The glass plate may be rotated about an axis parallel to the slit and it thus shifts the spectrum to one side or the other until the displaced feature comes into view at maximum density. The angle of rotation of the line-shifter measures the displacement, from which the magnitude of the sightline velocity may be deduced.

LIGHT FILTERS

Colour filters made of glass and other substances are often employed to transmit limited ranges of the spectrum. Their special uses are familiar to photographers. None of these filters, however, will pass a sufficiently narrow band to isolate a single spectral line, as in the spectrohelioscope. A new type of filter with a very narrow band-pass was first used by Öhman and has since been developed by Lyot and Evans. This is known as a mono-chromator, and its action is based upon the physical principles of interference and polarization. It consists of a composite prism built up of flat plates of clear quartz, each pair being separated by a sheet of polaroid. The white light is first made to vibrate in one plane by passage through one of the polaroids. The quartz plate then divides this light into two beams, an 'ordinary' beam vibrating in a plane parallel to the quartz crystal axis and an 'extraordinary' beam vibrating in a plane at 90° to the axis. When these two beams are brought back to the same plane of polarization by passage through the next polaroid sheet they are in a condition to interfere with one another, in consequence of their different velocities through the quartz. Some colours are thus removed by interference and the intermediate colours are reinforced. Thus, after its transmission through two polaroids and one quartz plate, the light has a spectrum consisting of evenly spaced bright and dark bands along its length. Passage of the remaining beam through further polaroids and quartz plates of increasing thickness, reduces the number of colour bands transmitted, until eventually one of the bands, centred on the line $H\alpha$ say, is sufficiently separated from its neighbours to be isolated from them by the simple expedient of interposing a plate of red glass.

This instrument contains no moving parts and requires no spectroscope for its use. It can be attached, like an eyepiece, to a small telescope and gives brilliant views of the chromosphere and prominences. On the other hand, it requires the most skilful construction and needs very precise temperature control when in use. A change of temperature of $1°$ C. alters the refractive index of the quartz by a sufficient amount to shift the narrow transmission band of the filter right off the centre of the $H\alpha$ line. It is being increasingly used for continuous studies of the chromosphere by cinematography. This type of filter does not allow us to photograph the spectrum of any outburst, like a flare or active prominence, which may unexpectedly appear. When we are observing with the spectrohelioscope and see such an event beginning we can at once bring the oscillating slits to rest (Fig. 3.1), and by a small rotation of the grating the spectrum of the feature is focused upon the photographic plate at P. We can thus obtain a permanent record showing many different lines in the spectrum, from which, by examination of their intensities, breadths and displacements, valuable information may be derived about the physical conditions in these outbursts. The spectra shown in Plate II were recorded in this way.

THE CHROMOSPHERE

Our first reaction to the sight of the chromosphere (Plate III) is one of amazement, that it can present such a contrasting spectacle to the almost featureless photosphere which is situated only a few thousand kilometres below. The general appearance is one of fine mottling, something like the skin of an orange. This is the normal condition in those regions where there is little activity. Here and there we also see brighter areas where the hydrogen atoms are emitting more intensely. These are the *plages*. They are always located in or near sunspot groups and they occur at a low atmospheric level. Scattered over the disk in long narrow lines are the *dark filaments*. The dark filaments are identical with the *prominences*. When they are seen standing up to great heights in elevation at the sun's limb they appear bright against the dark background of the sky. But the hydrogen light which a prominence emits is normally less intense than that of the chromosphere, and so, against the disk, it stands out dark by contrast with the latter. As the solar rotation carries round these tall filaments of gas we can follow their changing shapes from day to day with the spectrohelioscope, as they are presented at different angles to the line of sight, until eventually we see only their profiles at the sun's edge, and a few days later still they have disappeared behind the 'hill' (Fig. 3.3). Accurate photometry shows that they have the same brightness in all positions, though it is difficult to convince the eye that this is so. Close to sunspots one can also observe smaller dark markings, which the spectrohelioscope line-shifter shows are often in rapid motion and which are constantly changing in form, appearing and disappearing. These are the active sunspot prominences which we shall refer to later.

On rare occasions one may be fortunate enough to

63

witness the outburst of a truly remarkable phenomenon in the chromosphere above a large sunspot. This is a solar flare. In the space of a few minutes one of the bright plage areas may be completely transformed into a 'white-hot' mass of glowing patches and filaments. The rise in brightness may be extremely rapid, sometimes occurring in less than a minute, and it is followed by a slow decay lasting half an hour or more. Plate III was photographed during the great flare of 1946 July 25, which the author was fortunate in observing from start to finish. Such an event on the sun is profoundly stirring to watch. Indeed, it is difficult to control one's excitement sufficiently to carry out the elaborate drill of photography and measurement, which must be practised beforehand so that one is always ready to secure the maximum of information during these sudden and unpredictable occurrences. This particular cataclysm was located over the great sunspot which is illustrated in Fig. 2.4, and when fully developed extended over a distance of 800,000 km. (500,000 miles) in the solar atmosphere. As we shall see in a later chapter, intense flares set in operation a remarkable train of events which have immediate consequences upon the earth.

The lines of the Fraunhofer spectrum all possess an appreciable breadth and a characteristic structure. If we photograph the $H\alpha$ line with a sufficiently powerful spectrograph, we can measure the brightness at many points within the line. When such measures are plotted against the wavelengths we obtain a line *profile*, such as the heavy curve in Fig. 3.2. The line possesses a deep central core about 1 A. wide, together with wide sloping wings which slowly increase in brightness as we move away to either side, until they merge into the level of the continuous spectrum at distances of about 15 A. from the line centre. The $H\alpha$ line of the chromosphere is, therefore, about 30 A. wide.

64

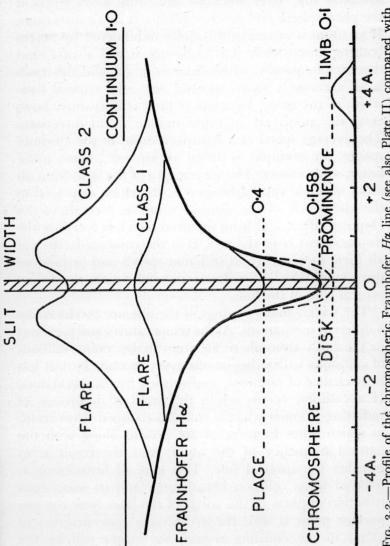

FIG. 3.2.—Profile of the chromospheric Fraunhofer Hα line (see also Plate II) compared with those of prominences, plages and flares. The intensity within the line is plotted vertically (continuous spectrum of photosphere = 1·0) and wavelength horizontally.

We recollect that the atoms contributing light to this so-called 'line' have absorbed light from lower levels in the photosphere and are re-emitting it in all directions. If an atom is at rest and is quite unhindered by neighbouring atoms while it is radiating, it will always emit the same frequency, within narrow limits, and the result is an excessively sharp spectral line—the natural line-width of the atom. In a gas at high temperature, however, the atoms are in rapid motion in all directions. The average speed of a hydrogen atom in the chromosphere, for example, is about 10 km./sec., some move faster, some slower. The wavelength of the light from an atom which is approaching us is, therefore, displaced to the violet side of the normal value as a result of the Doppler effect, and from an atom which is receding the displacement is to the red. It is the combined effect of all these movements, at different speeds and in random directions, which distributes the light over the broad central core of the line.

The wider, shallow wings of the line are produced by a different mechanism. At the temperatures and pressures in the sun's atmosphere an atom makes many millions of collisions with other atoms every second. It thus has little chance of radiating undisturbed by its neighbours. If a collision occurs while the atom is in process of radiating it emits what is called a damped wave-train, in which other frequencies are present along with the natural frequency of the atom; and the result is to broaden the spectral line. This kind of broadening is referred to as collision broadening, and its main contribution appears in the wings of the line. Now the important point is this, the greater the concentration of atoms in the emitting region, the larger will be the number of collisions and hence the broader the wings. The deeper we look down into the chromosphere the higher the gas density becomes; consequently we expect

66

the lower levels to contribute more light to the line wings than to the central core. Thus, if we move the selecting slit of the spectrohelioscope 1 A. to either side of the line centre, we obtain quite a different picture of the chromosphere from that which is seen when the slit is centrally placed on the core of the line. In this position of the slit we observe a lower and more turbulent level in which the mottling of the surface is much coarser than before, and we find that the high-level prominences have disappeared, for in them gas pressure is insufficient to produce broadening of the line by collisions.

The chromosphere may also be photographed by the light of other atoms besides those of hydrogen, such as the H and K lines of ionized calcium in the violet end of the spectrum and the various lines of helium. Each picture presents a somewhat different aspect, depending upon the concentration of the various atoms and the ease with which they are excited to emit radiation in the active sunspot regions. Problems of interpretation arise, many of which still await solution.

PROMINENCES

'The sky's unresting cloudland' is a source of perpetual interest and wonder to weather watchers on the earth. Although terrestrial clouds may be classified into many well-known forms, no two clouds are ever exactly alike. The solar clouds, or prominences, have been studied for a much shorter time. Their remarkable forms and motions, as revealed by the fascinating cinematograph pictures which have been taken in recent years, provide important clues to a fuller understanding of the physics of the solar atmosphere. There is a fundamental difference, however, between terrestrial clouds and solar prominences. Clouds consist of water droplets, or ice crystals; these are large particles which shine by scattering

sunlight of all wavelengths. In contrast, the prominences are hot, tenuous gases at a temperature of 10,000°–
20,000°. The luminosity of a prominence comes from its
atoms; these absorb light from the solar surface and then
re-emit it in discrete wavelengths. The prominence light
is, therefore, monochromatic and is similar in character
to that of a neon sign or mercury lamp.

A century ago prominences could only be seen when
the sun was totally eclipsed. Having observed the bright
emission lines in the spectra of prominences during the
memorable eclipse of 1868, Janssen (and later Lockyer
independently) discovered that prominences could be
seen at all times round the edge of the solar disk without
the intervention of an eclipse. All that was needed was a
spectroscope attached to a small telescope. Systematic
observations, begun by Respighi in 1869, were collected
and published up till 1911 in the *Memoirs of the Italian
Society of Spectroscopists*. These records, giving the daily
areas and positions of prominences seen in *elevation* at the
sun's limb, have been continued to the present day in the
publications of the Arcetri Observatory.

It soon became apparent that prominences varied both
in frequency and in solar latitude with the course of the
11-year cycle of sunspot activity. In each hemisphere
there are two principal prominence zones. The more
important, located in the sunspot belts, commences in
latitudes ± 30° one or two years after the minimum of
the sunspot cycle, and follows, with a lag of about 10°,
the latitude of greatest sunspot frequency in its slow
progress towards the equator. The number and size of
the prominences in this zone follow very closely the
figures for the sunspots. The second zone commences in
latitudes ± 45° at about the time of sunspot minimum
and moves towards the poles, reaching latitudes ± 75°
shortly after the following sunspot maximum, at which
period it is sometimes referred to as the 'polar crown' of

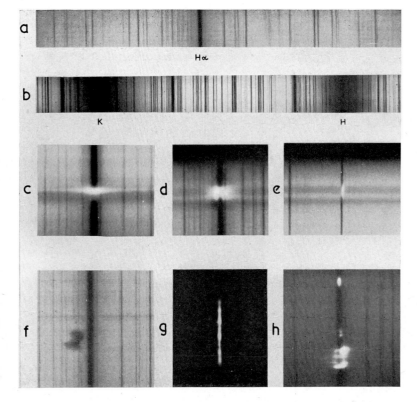

Plate II.—SOLAR SPECTRA

(a) Fraunhofer spectrum in region of $H\alpha$ (6,563 A.).

(b) Same, showing the H (3,968 A.) and K (3,934 A.) lines of ionized calcium.

(c, d) Emission lines of $H\alpha$ in intense flares.

(e) Emission line of He (6,678 A.) in flare.

(f) $H\alpha$ line of disk prominence displaced 3 A. to blue side by Doppler effect of motion in line of sight ($V =$ 140 km./sec. approach = 87 miles/sec.).

(g) $H\alpha$ line of quiescent prominence outside sun's limb.

(h) $H\alpha$ line of active prominence at sun's limb.

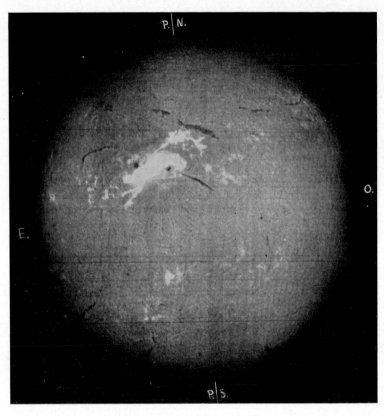

PLATE III.—CHROMOSPHERE AND GREAT FLARE

Photograph taken in hydrogen ($H\alpha$) light, Meudon, 1946 July 25, 17^h 32^m U.T. The development of this flare is illustrated in Fig. 8.6. (*Reproduced by courtesy of M. L. d'Azambuja.*)

prominences. Prominences are largest and most numerous in the high latitude zones about two years before the peak of the sunspots.

The early observers made a broad classification of prominences into two main types: (1) the stable *quiescent* prominences, frequenting both high and low latitudes, of great height and length, and composed in the main of hydrogen, helium and calcium vapour; (2) the *eruptive* prominences of short life, confined to the sunspot zones and exhibiting, in addition, the spectral lines of other metallic vapours.

So long as prominences could be observed only at the border of the sun's disk, for short periods when they were seen projected against the sky, little was known about their true shapes and sizes, about their life-histories and their special relations with sunspots. But now, by means of the daily photographs of the chromosphere, we can follow the passage of a prominence right across the disk, during the $13\frac{1}{2}$-day interval between its rising on the E limb and its setting on the W limb. A fortnight later it may be picked up again as it comes into view for a second time. Many new types have been discovered, of which the following are the most important.

Quiescent prominences.—These are among the most stable of all solar features. M. and Mme d'Azambuja, of Meudon Observatory, who have made a special study of their characteristics, find that many of them endure for five solar rotations before they break up, or, as happens in some cases, blow off violently from the sun and disappear into space.

As an example of extreme dimensions, we may mention the prominence generated by the great sunspot of 1946 February. This filament grew slowly to 1,900,000 km. in length, was in places 100,000 km. high, but no more than 10,000 km. thick on the average. It remained

F   69

visible until the end of July. (See Fig. 3.3.) Such prominences are tall and thin, and may be compared to a

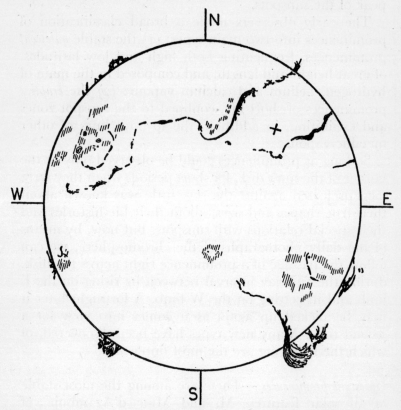

FIG. 3.3.—Limb and disk prominences seen through the spectrohelioscope (Sherborne, 11·30 U.T., 1946 May 28). The long prominences
in the N hemisphere were generated by the great sunspot of 1946
February (Plate I); *cross* marks former position of sunspot. Vertical
hatching represents regions of bright hydrogen (plages) associated with
sunspot groups. The prominences are drawn to scale (solar diameter=
1,400,000 km.).

row of trees, meandering in a crooked line across the
country-side. When the trees pass over the sky-line, their
appearance will be very different according as we happen

Fig. 3.4.—Prominence types: (a) Quiescent 'row of trees' (Edinburgh, 1951 Sept. 27); (b) 'Leaking' coronal funnel (Edinburgh, 1951 Oct. 20); (c) Interactive prominences (Sherborne, 1946 June 19); (d) Common active (Sherborne, 1947 July 12); (e) Loops over sunspots (Yerkes, 1907 Aug. 14); (f) Active sunspot prominence (Sherborne, 1940 March 8); (g) Surge blown out by flare (Edinburgh, 1949 Nov. 19); (h) Flare surge (Edinburgh, 1951 May 10).

to be looking along the line or across the line. Likewise, a prominence filament seen at the sun's limb will present different aspects, according to how it is orientated with respect to the observer's vision. It may have the appearance of a long row of trees, as in Fig. 3.4*a*, or of a single tree, if seen end on.

Active prominences.—These are tall tree-like structures, from the tops of which thin ropes of matter flow out horizontally and then curve downwards towards some centre of attraction in the photosphere (Fig. 3.4*b* and *d*). Condensations of matter which can be seen following one another along these trajectories look like beads slipping along a curved wire. Their movements strongly suggest that the material is being constrained to travel along lines of force in a magnetic field. The streamers may be as much as 100,000 km. in length and the velocities in them are of the order of 100 km./sec.

Two adjacent prominences may feed streamers across the gap between their tops, the matter flowing along separate trajectories in opposite directions (Fig. 3.4*c*). Such prominences are said to be 'interactive'.

Eruptive prominences.—An active prominence sometimes sheds its material so violently into a near-by centre of attraction that it is torn up by the roots, so to speak. It then ascends to a height of several hundred thousand kilometres, most of its material being sucked back into the attractive centre. These are known as quasi-eruptives. The true eruptives, on the other hand, blow right off into space without any visible sign of return. Pettit, who has made a special study of these types, has found outward velocities varying from about 50 km./sec. to a maximum of 728 km./sec. One eruptive was followed outwards to a distance greater than the sun's diameter before it faded away. In Plate IV we see an eruptive arch which was moving outwards from the sun at 500 km./sec.

The great distortions of the spectral lines in this case show that the two legs of the arch were spinning in contrary directions, like the opposite sides of a smoke ring. We cannot be certain whether this eruptive matter gets trapped in the corona or whether it passes on into outer space.

Sunspot prominences.—Large and active sunspot groups generate characteristic prominence types in their vicinity. First, we have (*a*) the *inflowing streamers.* Matter appears to 'condense into visibility' in the corona above a sunspot and rains down in thin graceful streamers which are drawn in towards the spot, becoming nearly vertical as they disappear into the penumbral region. Guidance by the sunspot magnetic field is strongly suggested. Velocities in these trajectories are of the order of 50 km./sec. (*b*) *Loops and arches* are rare and beautiful forms (Fig. 3.4*e*). They are abnormally bright and are only found in association with highly flare-active sunspots. Matter usually flows down both sides of a loop at once. (*c*) Large sunspots also generate *flanking prominences* (Fig. 3.4*f*). These slowly extend outwards from the spot region, and after some weeks turn into the long quiescent filaments which have been described above. While they are still in the vicinity of the parent sunspot they feed streamers from their tops down into centres of attraction located in the spot group, and they show periodical bursts of internal activity lasting for several hours.

Certain small areas near sunspots have the power of ejecting *surges*. These may be described as jets of highly luminous material which rise in nearly vertical trajectories (sometimes curved) to heights of 100,000 km. or more. The ascent is followed by a slower recoil, often along the same path. Several different types have been noted and the largest are those which are shot out from flares (Fig. 3.4*g* and *h*). In the latter the initial upward

73

velocity may be as high as 500 km./sec. Surges are short-lived, lasting for 20 minutes or so, and they may follow one another in a succession from the same active locality.

Cinematograph pictures of prominences are usually taken at intervals of 30 seconds over a period of some hours. When these films are projected at a rate of 20 frames per second all the phenomena are speeded up 600 times. In this way we gain a most vivid impression of the development and internal motions of the various types. It is immediately obvious that we are witnessing movements of a kind which have no parallel on the earth. For this reason physicists who are interested in the movements of ionized gases in the presence of magnetic fields have studied these films with great attention, but their interpretation is still in its infancy.

One fact is clear, however; the visible matter in most prominences is moving *downwards* towards the solar surface. Some prominences rain matter down through thin trajectories for long periods, yet their bulk does not diminish, and it is, therefore, evident that they are being continually replenished from above. We must suppose that this material which flows in at the tops of the prominences comes from the corona where it was previously ionized and invisible. As soon as these gas atoms enter the prominence region, where the temperature is lower and the pressure higher than in the surrounding corona, they gain electrons and are enabled to radiate in the characteristic spectral lines of the prominences. The coronal gases are much too hot to be visible in the ordinary spectral lines, and Hoyle has consequently put forward the view that prominences are simply regions of local cooling in the corona. There is much to commend this idea, and, as we shall see in a later section, prominences appear to be closely related to the structure and brightness of the corona in their immediate vicinity.

Since the material in most prominences is falling, it is

evident that what comes down must first have gone up. How then does this invisible, ionized matter collect in the corona before its visible descent through the prominence begins? Prof. D. H. Menzel, of Harvard, and Dr. W. Orr Roberts, of Climax, have photographed and studied more prominence films than any other workers in this field. They believe that matter is being continually 'evaporated' off from the chromosphere into the corona, and in support of this conclusion they point to the small and numerous prominences which they call *spicules*. The spicules have the appearance of bubbles of gas which are ejected from the chromosphere and fade into invisibility as they reach the corona.

Prof. Menzel considers that all prominences are supported against gravity by electromagnetic forces, and that these forces are also responsible for the remarkable forms and motions which are observed. If this is so, it is natural that those prominences which are found near sunspots, where the magnetic and electric fields are so much stronger, should differ markedly from the types which are found elsewhere.

THE CORONA

For a few minutes during the black-out caused by a total eclipse the sun is seen to be surrounded by a halo of silvery white light (Plate V). This halo is the corona— the extended outer atmosphere of the sun. Close to the sun's limb the intensity of the coronal light is one-millionth part of the brightness at the centre of the solar disk, and its intensity falls off rapidly outwards, so that at 1·5 solar radii the brightness has diminished to about 1 per cent of this value. Still further out faint streamers can often be seen extending to distances of several times the sun's diameter.

For close on a century the study of the corona was

confined to those rare occasions when the light of the photosphere was blotted out by the disk of the moon. It was, therefore, visible on the average for no more than one minute in each year. At all other times its faint luminosity was overpowered by the intense glare of sunlight which is scattered by the earth's atmosphere. Many unsuccessful attempts were made to photograph the corona without an eclipse; until, in 1930, the French astronomer Bernard Lyot began a systematic search for the causes underlying these failures. Lyot showed that there were two principal reasons why the coronal light is not normally visible. First, atmospheric dust forms, by diffraction and scattering, a bright halo round the sun; even in clear weather this halo may be 50 or 100 times brighter than the light of the corona. Secondly, an ordinary telescope or camera lens, when directed towards the sun, produces, by diffraction from its circular edge and from small imperfections in the glass itself, another halo—an instrumental halo—which is also brighter than the corona which it is desired to photograph. Lyot reduced the brightness of these scattered light haloes in two ways: (a) by constructing a camera of new design, using lenses of such perfection as to reduce the scattered light in the instrument, and (b) by taking the whole apparatus to a height of 9,400 feet at Pic du Midi in the Pyrenees, at which elevation the scattering by atmospheric dust is no longer such a serious menace.

Fig. 3.5 shows the principal parts of Lyot's coronagraph. The plano-convex lens A, constructed of the most transparent glass and free from blemishes, forms an image of the sun on the circular blackened disk at B. This disk is just sufficiently large to intercept the direct light of the photosphere; a field-lens C, placed behind the disk, forms an image A'A" of the lens A upon the circular diaphragm D, which also carries a small screen E at its centre. The diaphragm D masks out the halo of light diffracted from the borders of lens A, and the screen E removes the spots of light caused by reflections of sunlight from the two surfaces of this lens. An achromatic lens at F serves to focus the light of the corona, now freed from scattered light, upon the photographic plate at B′B″. Instruments of this type are in use at many high altitude stations, from which observations are made every clear day of the bright inner parts of the white corona and of its characteristic emission spectrum lines. The outer extensions of the corona are still too faint to be seen except at times of a total eclipse.

The nature of the corona has long been an enigma, and many of its problems are still unsolved. It is natural

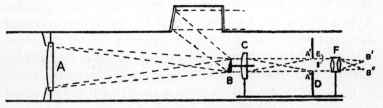

FIG. 3.5.—The Lyot coronagraph.

to ask why the sun should possess an outer atmosphere, extending so far beyond the limits of the chromosphere, which may be regarded as the atmosphere proper. The light of the corona is white, in contrast to that of the chromosphere which we have seen is composed of discrete wavelengths. This suggests that the material of the corona shines by scattering the sunlight which falls upon it. Now, particles of atomic size scatter blue light more effectively than other colours. Our terrestrial sky is blue, not white. The coronal matter, however, is highly ionized, that is to say its atoms are split up into positive ions and negative electrons. These charged particles respond to the electrical vibrations of the solar light passing outwards through them. The very light electrons bob about like corks in this sea of waves, whereas the positive

77

ions, which are several thousand times more massive, lumber up and down more slowly like tramp steamers. The readier response of the free electrons causes them to scatter the incident radiations in all directions much more efficiently than the heavier ions. Since they can respond to all frequencies, the light which they send us is similar to that which they receive from the sun. But there is one important difference; the sunlight falling upon the coronal electrons possesses in its spectrum many absorption lines—the Fraunhofer lines which have been imprinted on the solar light in its passage through the reversing layer. The light we receive by electron scattering from the inner corona contains no trace of these lines. Where have they gone? There is only one conceivable answer. We have seen that the radiation received from an atom has its normal frequency only if the atom has no relative motion along the line of sight. Light from a cloud of atoms, all moving in random directions, gives a broadened spectral line, as a result of the individual Doppler shifts. If light of a single frequency is incident upon a cloud of high-speed electrons, the scattered light received from them will, likewise, be spread over a wide band of frequencies, depending upon their velocities. And in an atmosphere composed of ions and free electrons, the electrons will move one hundred times faster than the heavier ions. We conclude that the coronal electrons are moving so fast that they blur out the spectral lines in the light they scatter. An average speed of about 7,500 km./sec. would enable them to do this. Such speeds imply a gas temperature of 1,000,000 degrees!

This result may seem at first sight quite fantastic, especially when we recollect that the temperature of the solar surface is no more than 6,000°, and that of the prominences, which reach high into the corona, is only twice or three times as great. It may be thought to cast doubt on Grotrian's theory of electron scattering in the corona. Yet, as we shall see, there are a variety of ways in which the temperature can be found, without recourse to this theory, and the results are all in reasonable agreement. Moreover, this high temperature provides the clue to our initial query—Why does the corona extend so far away from the sun? Other factors, like gravity and molecular weight, being the same, the depth of an atmosphere depends only upon its temperature. The higher the temperature the more tenuous and extended is the atmosphere.

Although the coronal light is predominantly white and gives a continuous spectrum, this spectrum is crossed by a limited number of emission lines. The six brightest were photographed by Lockyer during the solar eclipse of 1898 in India. In all, twenty-nine bright lines are known, whose wavelengths are given in Table IV. For forty years the origin of the coronal emission lines remained one of the great unsolved puzzles of solar physics. Their positions in the spectrum failed to correspond with the lines of any known substances. They were tentatively attributed to a new element—coronium. However, later theoretical work showed that there was no room in the periodic table for this new element coronium, and that the unique emissions were much more likely to arise from some quite common element whose atoms, under the extreme conditions of bombardment existing in the corona, had been stripped of many of their planetary electrons, giving a spectrum different from any observable in the laboratory. Acting upon a suggestion of Prof. Grotrian, Edlén, the Swedish physicist, was able to calculate in 1940 that the wavelengths of the coronal lines were precisely those to be expected from atoms of iron, calcium and nickel which had lost from ten to fifteen electrons. The wavelengths predicted by theory were in such perfect agreement with those which had been measured from the spectra that there could no longer be any reasonable doubt that the identifications were correct. In Table IV a summary is given of the chief properties of these remarkable lines.

TABLE IV

Emission lines in the coronal spectrum

Wavelength in angstroms	Approximate intensity	Identification	Ionization potential (electron-volts)
3328	1	Ca XII	589
3388	16	Fe XIII	325
3454	2	—	—
3534	—	—	—
3601	2	Ni XVI	455
3643	—	Ni XIII	350
3801	—	—	—
3987	1	Fe XI	261
3997	—	—	—
4086	1	Ca XIII	655
4231	3	Ni XII	318
4311	—	—	—
4351	—	—	—
4359	—	A XIV	682
4412	—	—	—
4567	1	—	—
4586	—	—	—
5116	3	Ni XIII	350
5303	100	Fe XIV	355
5445	—	—	—
5536	—	A X	421
5694	1	Ca XV	814
6375	13	Fe X	233
6702	3	Ni XV	422
7060	2	Fe XV	390
7892	13	Fe XI	261
8024	1	Ni XV	422
10747	55	Fe XIII	325
10798	35	Fe XIII	325

The brightest is the green line (5303) which arises from *Fe* XIV, that is to say, an atom of iron which has lost *thirteen* of its planetary electrons. Another bright line is 6375 in the red end of the spectrum; this comes from

Fe X, an iron atom which has lost *nine* electrons. In the last column are tabulated the corresponding ionization potentials. These figures represent simply the energies in electron-volts which the colliding atoms must possess in order to strip off electrons to the observed extent. These high ionization energies also require temperatures of about 1,000,000° K. It is interesting to notice that the red and green lines, which demand the lowest energies for their production, are usually in evidence almost all round the sun's disk, whereas the yellow line (5694) is only observed, as Waldmeier and Roberts have shown, over sunspots near the sun's limb. This line requires the highest energy of all (814 e.v.), from which we conclude that the hottest parts of the corona are to be found over active sunspots.

Let us now summarize the evidence for the existence of this very high temperature within the corona:

(1) Heavy atoms in a low pressure gas should give narrow spectral lines, but we find that the emission lines are about 1 A. wide, indicating high thermal velocities.

(2) The energies of collision needed to produce the highly ionized atoms.

(3) The blurring out of the Fraunhofer lines in the light scattered by the electrons.

(4) The great extent of the corona, assumed to be due to high atomic velocities balancing the gravitational pull.

(5) The absence in the corona of low temperature spectral lines, such as appear in the prominences.

(6) The characteristics of the propagation of short-wave radio within the corona, as referred to in Chapter VIII.

None of these methods taken by themselves can yield a very precise value for the temperature, but all are in

agreement about the order of magnitude, which is
1,000,000° K. While the true figure may be twice, or
even one-half, this value, it is unlikely to lie outside that
range. Herein lies the great interest of the corona. It is
the hottest matter in the visible universe. The centres of
the stars may be hotter, but we have no hope of seeing
inside. The corona, right on our door-step, provides a
unique high-temperature laboratory where the physicists
can enjoy themselves. Little wonder that, following upon
this unexpected discovery, the investigation of the corona
has attracted so much attention.

How is this high temperature maintained? On this
issue there has been much speculation, but as yet little
agreement, among the astrophysicists. Bondi, Hoyle and
Lyttleton believe that the heating arises from the capture
of interstellar dust as the sun sweeps through space. The
gravitational pull would cause these particles to fall into
the sun's atmosphere with a velocity of about 600
km./sec. The particle energies would then be distributed
as heat throughout the coronal matter; in other words
the corona is being heated from the top downwards.
However, it is still uncertain whether sufficient material
could be captured in this way. Moreover, the shape and
extent of the corona, both of which vary with the 11-year
cycle of solar activity (see Plate V), suggest an internal
rather than an external origin for the heating. We have
also seen that the hottest regions of the corona are those
connected with the sunspot zones.

If we assume that the corona is being heated from
below, we are faced with a fundamental difficulty,
namely that heat cannot flow from a cool body—the
photosphere at 6,000°—to a hot body—the corona. This
would be contrary to the second law of thermodynamics.
Some authorities have maintained that matter much
hotter than that of the photosphere is being blown up
into the corona from great depths within the sun. There

is no observational evidence for this; and such matter would almost certainly expand and cool, like the rising material within sunspots, before it could reach the coronal space.

It now seems fairly certain that the coronal heating must arise through some novel mechanism which will circumvent the second law of thermodynamics and transfer energy from the cooler surface regions to the hotter corona. Nearer home we are familiar with many small-scale examples of this kind of process. For example, when we switch on an electric light, energy is transferred by means of an electric current (flow of electrons), from the steam in a boiler to the much hotter filament of the lamp. The process may be inefficient in terms of energy conversion; nevertheless it generates the desired temperature. According to Alfvén the corona is heated by electric currents in just this way. The solar currents may be generated by the vortical motion in sunspots which can bring about high voltages between different points on the sun's surface. In a highly ionized gas the currents will flow most easily along the lines of magnetic force, which, under certain conditions, may form complete circuits lying partly within the corona. In our simple terrestrial analogy the sunspot whirl takes the place of the dynamo and the corona represents the filament of the lamp. Prof. Alfvén also believes that the mysterious prominence filaments are visible examples of these currents, that is to say streams of charged particles moving along the magnetic lines of force between two points having a high potential difference.

Whatever may be the outcome of these interesting ideas, it is evident that we have moved very far indeed from the older picture of the sun as a glowing ball of gas quietly radiating its heat into space. Its turbulent atmosphere is the seat of remarkable physical phenomena which were unthought of thirty years ago.

Dr. von Klüber's fine photograph (Plate V), taken during the 1952 eclipse at Khartoum, shows another very puzzling feature of the corona—the coronal rays. At times of sunspot minimum the rays have their greatest extension in the equatorial regions; near the maximum they are shorter and more uniformly distributed in latitude, though they usually avoid the two poles. They are so much fainter than the inner corona that their visibility is confined to times of eclipses. We then see them projected against the sky, but, of course, they protrude from the sun in all directions and rotate with it. If we stick a number of knitting needles in different directions through a rubber ball we have quite a good model of the coronal rays. They appear to be intimately connected with the prominences which lie below them. This is not obvious from photographs, because the long exposures needed to show the rays greatly over-expose the brighter inner corona and prominences. But composite photographs and drawings, such as those of Fig. 3.6, show the connection very clearly. The coronal material often forms a series of arches over the prominence with a relatively dark space between the two. Above these the corona forms a petal, tapering upwards and issuing in a long narrow ray. In Plate V the ray on the east side of the sun could be traced out to a distance of six times the sun's diameter. The appearance of these rays is strongly suggestive of the focusing action which magnetic and electric fields of suitable types may have upon moving charged particles. We may have here an analogy with the focusing of the electron beam in an electron microscope or in a cathode ray tube.

Allen has gone further and has produced some evidence that the coronal rays may be the trajectories of charged particles which on occasions reach out as far as the earth's orbit. If they were suitably directed in space the solar rotation would then cause them to sweep

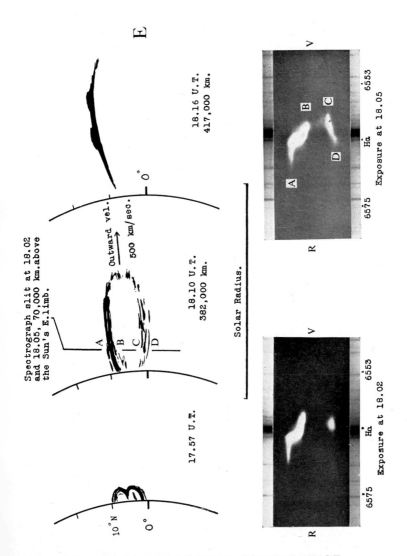

PLATE IV.—GREAT ERUPTIVE PROMINENCE

From observations made at Sherborne, 1947 June 11. Motion across the line of sight (*above*) at 500 km./sec. (312 miles/sec.). Doppler distortions of the *H*α line (*below*) indicate that the legs of the arch were spinning like a smoke ring. The sightline speeds are: A + 330 km./sec. (+ 210 miles/sec.), B − 150 km./sec. (− 95 miles/sec.), C − 180 km./sec. (− 110 miles/sec.) and D + 90 km./sec.(+ 55 miles/sec.) (− is towards, and + away from, the observer).

PLATE V.—CORONA AT SUNSPOT MAXIMUM
AND MINIMUM

Top: The corona at sunspot maximum (1927 June 29).
  (*Reproduced by courtesy of the Director, Hamburg Observatory.*)
Below: The corona near sunspot minimum (1952 February 25).
  (*Reproduced by courtesy of Dr. H. von Klüber.*)

across the earth at 27-day intervals. Many years ago Bartels drew attention to certain minor disturbances in the earth's magnetic field which were presumed, by

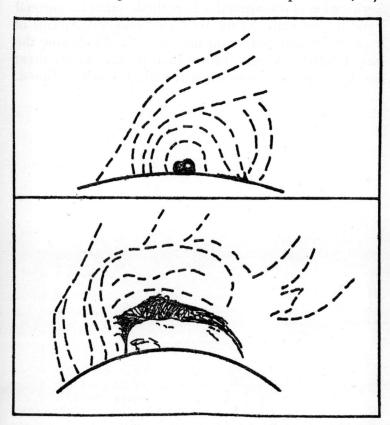

Fig. 3.6.—Relationship of coronal structure to that of underlying prominences, suggesting the action of local magnetic fields. *Top:* Based on drawings by Mr. W. H. Wesley from eclipse plates, 1901 May 18. *Bottom:* Based on drawings by Miss A. M. Crommelin from eclipse plates, 1919 May 29.

reason of their 27-day recurrences, to have a solar origin. Moreover, these magnetic M-storms, so called to distinguish them from the non-recurrent great magnetic storms, are most pronounced during the period of minimum sunspot activity, and at this time also the coronal rays are most extended in the sun's equatorial plane. The verification of this attractive hypothesis—that the coronal rays are the cause of the terrestrial magnetic storms of type M—will require some new method of following the rays from day to day, rather than waiting to see them on those rare occasions when the sun is totally eclipsed.

CHAPTER IV

The Ionosphere

EXPLORING THE IONOSPHERE

HALF a century has passed since Marconi, on 1901 December 12, succeeded, at his first attempt, in transmitting and receiving wireless waves across the Atlantic, from Poldhu in England to St. John's in Newfoundland. This great achievement completely vindicated Marconi's faith that the electric rays, as they were then called, would bend round the globe of the earth, making communication possible between any two points on the surface of the planet, an opinion he had held for many years in the face of opposition from a number of mathematical physicists. These people very naturally said that the radio waves, being of the same nature as light, could not be expected to bend round an obstacle so large in comparison to their wavelength.

Six months later, Oliver Heaviside made his famous suggestion of the existence in the earth's upper atmosphere of an electrically conducting layer, which would prevent the dissipation of the waves out into space and would guide them round the spherical surface of the earth. He said: 'There may possibly be a sufficiently conducting layer in the upper air. If so, the waves will, so to speak, catch on to it more or less. Then the guidance will be by the sea on the one side and the upper air on the other.' Very similar ideas were put forward in rather more detail by Kennelly at about the same time; and greater precision was later given to them by Eccles, who supposed the conductivity of the layer to be due to the presence of ions and electrons, formed by the action of solar ultra-violet light.

The first direct evidence for the existence of the Kennelly-Heaviside layer (or the *E*-layer, as it is now called) had to await the experiments of Appleton and Barnett in 1925. These two workers observed interference maxima and minima between the direct (or ground) wave and the wave reflected from the *E*-layer when the frequency of a broadcast transmitter 140 km. (87 miles) distant was slowly varied by a known amount. Their results proved that reflection was occurring at a height of about 100 km. (62 miles) above the earth.

Nearly all the subsequent work of exploring the ionized layers has been carried out by vertical incidence sounding, a technique first evolved by Breit and Tuve in America. In the methods which have been employed all over the world during the last 20 years or so, pulses of radio frequency, about 100 microseconds [1] long, are transmitted vertically upwards from a ground station and their reflections from the particular ionized region are received back at the same station after an interval $2t$, representing the group time of flight. The transmitted pulse and its 'echoes' are displayed as 'blips' on a cathode-ray tube and the distance between them can be recorded continuously on photographic film. The semi-interval t provides a measure of the equivalent height (h') of reflection. The height of the layer is found to depend upon the exploring frequency (f) of the radio waves; and graphs showing the (h', f) relation have for many years provided the most important basic information for ionospheric studies. In Fig. 4.1 for example, the heights of reflection in kilometres are plotted vertically and the frequencies of the exploring radio waves are plotted horizontally. This graph represents conditions at

[1] 1 microsecond = 1 millionth of a second.

noon during the winter months in the south of England. We see that, as the exploring frequency is increased, reflection first takes place from the E-layer at a height of about 110 km. But when the frequency reaches a value of about 3 Mc./s. (100 metres wavelength)[1] the waves penetrate the E-layer and begin to be reflected from the F-layer at a height of about 230 km. Further increase of frequency gives reflections from steadily increasing heights, until, at a frequency of about 10 Mc./s. (30 metres), penetration of the F-layer is obtained and the signals fail to return. At noon in summer, conditions are somewhat different: the F-layer then appears to consist of two overlapping regions, referred to as the F_1- and F_2-layers, having minimum equivalent heights of 200 km. (125 miles) and 330 km. (205 miles) respectively.

In fact, Fig. 4.1 shows only the behaviour of the reflections of the ordinary ray. Under the influence of the earth's magnetic field each ionized layer becomes a doubly-refracting medium. This means that a beam of radio waves entering it is split into two parts, an ordinary ray and an extraordinary ray, of differing polarization. The critical frequencies of penetration, as measured by the return of the extraordinary ray, are somewhat greater than those shown in the diagram.

The critical penetration frequency of a layer is a most valuable quantity, because the maximum electron concentration within the layer may be derived from it, the two quantities being connected by the simple relation

$$N = 1 \cdot 24 \times 10^{-8} f_0{}^2,$$

where N is the maximum number of free electrons per cubic centimetre, and f_0 is the measured critical frequency in cycles per second for the ordinary polarized

[1] A frequency of 1 megacycle per second (Mc./s.) = 1 million vibrations per second; 1 kilocycle per second (Kc./s.) = 1 thousand vibrations per second. Wavelength (in metres) = 300/Frequency (in Mc./s.).

ray. In other words, the critical frequency is proportional to the square root of the number of electrons. Thus for winter noon conditions in the south of England the maximum electron concentration of the E-layer is about 10^5 electrons per cubic centimetre, while at summer noon the value is some 50 per cent greater. For the F-layer in winter the maximum electron concentration has a larger value, in the region of 10^6 electrons per cubic centimetre.

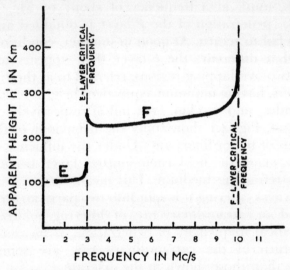

FIG. 4.1.—Heights of reflection of radio waves of different frequencies from the E- and F-layers (winter noon conditions in the south of England).

The ionization of the D region, at a level of 70–90 km., has been less completely explored. The echo, or radar, technique which has been so successfully employed for sounding the upper layers is inconvenient at the low frequencies needed for D-layer reflections. Our knowledge of this layer has been mainly derived from reflections at oblique incidence of very long radio waves, following the interference methods introduced by Ratcliffe and his collaborators at Cambridge. The influence of this layer upon radio propagation round the globe is very great, since it forms the main stratum of ionospheric absorption for waves which traverse it in passing to and from the higher E- and F-layers. As we shall see later, it is also of great importance in the study of solar-terrestrial relations, for it is here that the extra-ionization occurs which is caused by the burst of ultra-violet light emitted from a solar flare. We must not think of the layers as having sharp boundaries. The D- and E-layers are many kilometres thick; and the number of free electrons increases slowly to a maximum in the middle of each layer and decreases again on the other side as we pass through. The F_2-layer is very much deeper than the others.

In Table V are collected together some of the principal facts about these ionized regions.

TABLE V

Layer	Average height in kilometres	Approximate number of free electrons per cubic centimetre	Radio bands reflected at oblique incidence	
			Frequency	Wavelength: metres
F_2	350*	$\left.\begin{array}{c}10^6\\2{\cdot}5\times10^5\end{array}\right\}$	30–1·5 Mc./s.	Short waves 10–200
F_1	220*			
E	120	$\left\{\begin{array}{l}1{\cdot}5\times10^5 \text{ (day)}\\1{\cdot}0\times10^4 \text{ (night)}\end{array}\right.$	1500–500 Kc./s.	Medium waves 200–600
D	80	10^2–10^4	500–10 Kc./s.	Long waves 600–30000

* The F_2 layer is very diffuse; the F_1- and F_2-layers merge at night.

SOLAR CONTROL OF THE IONIZED LAYERS

The action of the sun's ultra-violet light upon the upper atmosphere can be represented in a simple way by Fig. 4.2.

There are two principal reactions involved. A quantum of light has energy $h\nu$, where h is Planck's constant and v is the frequency. When the product hv is large enough, as in the ultra-violet, the quantum impinging upon an atmospheric molecule, say of oxygen, will split it up into two neutral atoms. This process is called photo-dissociation. At somewhat greater energies, a planetary electron may be knocked right out of an atom, producing two charged particles, a positive ion and a free electron. This is known as photo-ionization. It is the number of these free electrons present in any layer which

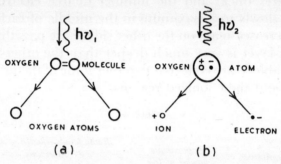

FIG. 4.2.—Action of solar ultra-violet light in the upper atmosphere: (a) photo-dissociation—oxygen molecule separates into two oxygen atoms by absorbing a light quantum of low energy; (b) photo-ionization—oxygen atom split up to form a positive ion and negative electron by absorption of a quantum of higher energy.

determines its power to reflect, or to absorb, the radio waves which fall upon it. We still know very little about the precise nature of the reactions taking place in any given layer, or even what atoms are involved, but it is clear that when the sun's light is cut off at night-time the positive ions and electrons begin to re-combine, and the number of free electrons decreases.

By the year 1935 it had become evident from the radio-sounding results that the critical frequencies, and therefore the number of free electrons, in the E- and F-layers, were subject to a marked solar control. First, the critical frequencies were found to depend, as was to be expected, upon (a) the daily, and (b) the seasonal variations in the sun's altitude. The varying inclination of the solar radiation could easily be allowed for by calculating the value of the layer 'character figure'. This quantity—$(f_0)^4/\cos \chi$, in which f_0 is the noon critical frequency and χ is the sun's zenith distance at the time—should be proportional to the ionizing power of the solar ultra-violet light when the sun is overhead. Now, when the character figures for the E- and F-layers had been plotted by Appleton and Naismith for a period of eight years a most surprising result was deduced. The character figure for each layer, and by inference also the solar ultra-violet radiation, was found to vary in sympathy with the sunspot relative number, that is to say with the 11-year cycle of solar activity. Between the sunspot minimum period of 1933–34 and the maximum period of 1937–38 the intensity of the radiation responsible for the formation of the E-layer was found to have increased by a factor of 2·2 and that for the F_1-layer by a somewhat larger amount. The number of free electrons varies as the square root of the intensity of the ionizing radiation. For the E-layer, therefore, the number of free electrons increases, between sunspot minimum and maximum, in the ratio $\sqrt{2\cdot2}$ which is 1·5, that is an increase of 50 per cent.

This result was quite unexpected, nor had it been foreseen by the solar physicists. On the contrary, the long series of careful measurements of the solar constant made by Abbot and later workers had shown that, in the region of the spectrum accessible to direct observation at ground level, the sun's output of light and heat was remarkably steady and showed no changes which could be attributed with certainty to the 11-year sunspot cycle. Hence, it was now clear that, at least in those unobservable (ultra-violet) wavelengths responsible for the formation and control of the ionized regions, the sun must be regarded as a variable star.

Whereabouts on the sun does this ultra-violet light originate, and what is its wavelength? Are there perhaps a number of different wavelengths involved, each being responsible for the ionization of one kind of atom, or molecule, in the high atmosphere before that particular light is completely absorbed? Such questions take us right into the field of active solar and ionospheric research, so that it is premature to try to give complete answers.

Allen has sought with considerable success to relate the changes in critical frequencies of the E-, F_1- and F_2-layers to changes in sunspot number, or to other solar features depending upon them. He finds evidence that the solar ultra-violet light consists of two parts. There is a variable part, whose intensity follows very closely the changes in sunspot number, and a steady part which is independent of the sunspots. He has shown that the variable part originates either in the sunspots themselves, or in the active regions surrounding them, and the constant part comes presumably from the whole solar disk. It must be the latter which is effective in maintaining the supply of electrons in the ionospheric layers for the long periods when there are no sunspots, as happens for weeks or even months at a time during the minimum years of solar activity. At time of maximum, the variable and the steady parts contribute about equal shares, so that the total intensity of the ultra-violet light is then about twice as great as at time of minimum.

In Allen's diagram (Fig. 4.3) the variations of critical frequency for the E-, F_1- and F_2-layers are shown for the years 1937–44. We can see that the changes occurring in the three layers are strikingly similar, and that they follow fairly closely the variations of sunspot number. But this does not necessarily mean that the ultra-violet

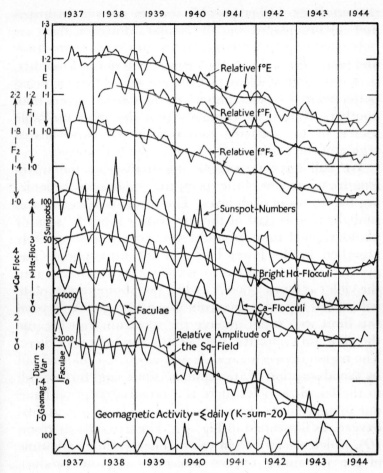

FIG. 4.3.—Variations of relative critical frequencies, sunspot numbers, flocculi (plages), faculae, relative S_q amplitude and geomagnetic activity, 1937–44. Reproduced from *Terrestrial Magnetism and Atmospheric Electricity*, **51**, 1, 1946, by courtesy of Prof. C. W. Allen and the editors.

light originates in the spots themselves. We recollect that the centre of a sunspot is a much cooler place than the rest of the sun's surface and it is unlikely, therefore, that it will emit more short-wave radiation than its

95

surroundings. Other possible sources are the hydrogen and calcium plages, and the faculae. However, these are only secondary manifestations of sunspot activity itself, and each follows closely the variations in sunspot number, so that it is impossible to pick out any one of them as being better related to the changes in the ionized layers than another. Waldmeier considers that the most probable source of the variable radiation is the super-heated region of the corona immediately above a sunspot.

We still have no precise information of the wavelengths, or regions of the spectrum, responsible for ionizing the atoms in each layer. The theorists disagree; and sunlight in this part of the spectrum cannot be seen or photographed from ground level, since it is completely absorbed in the lower layers of the atmosphere. The average eye is sensitive to wavelengths extending into the violet as far as 3,900 A., while the photographic plate will record the solar spectrum down to 2,900 A. Beyond this limit we cannot observe the spectrum, not because the plate isn't sensitive, but because the light isn't there. The region between 2,900 A. and 2,000 A. is blotted out by the absorption of atmospheric ozone, and further still in the far ultra-violet there is a broad absorption band due to molecular oxygen which is dissociated into atomic oxygen, as illustrated in Fig. 4.2. The free oxygen atoms (O), which are formed in this manner, collide with some of the remaining oxygen molecules (O_2) to produce molecules of ozone (O_3). The ozone is distributed at all heights up to about 60 km. and has its greatest concentration at 30 km. above the earth, a region of the atmosphere which is consequently known as the ozonosphere. The total amount of ozone is small, but its absorptive power is very great. If it were all concentrated at sea-level under normal pressure it would amount to a layer only a few millimetres thick.

The principal facts concerning the ozone layer were

discovered by Dobson twenty-five years ago, and his work was verified in a remarkable way shortly after the war. Rockets of the V_2 type were sent up from White Sands to heights of about 100 km. (62 miles). Each carried a small spectrograph, designed at the American Naval Research Laboratory, which recorded on films the spectrum of sunlight in the far ultra-violet during the ascents. The films were later recovered intact from among the twisted mass of debris where the rocket had landed. The spectra showed little extension towards shorter wavelengths until the rockets had penetrated above the level of greatest ozone concentration at 30 km. Thereafter, a new region of the solar spectrum was revealed, extending down to 2,200 A. when the rocket had reached a height of about 90 km., and brought into view many unknown Fraunhofer lines. It seems to be only a matter of time before penetration of the *E*- and *F*-layers will be similarly achieved, yielding direct information about the solar radiations which are effective in ionizing these regions.

THE PROPAGATION OF RADIO WAVES

Wireless waves which are radiated from a transmitter may reach a distant receiving station in two quite different ways. First, there is the ground-wave which follows the shortest path over the earth's surface between transmitter and receiver. Secondly, waves which travel upwards into the atmosphere are reflected by one or other of the ionized layers and arrive at the receiving point in a downward direction.

The power of an ionized layer to bend back radio waves to earth in this fashion depends upon the number of free electrons present and upon the frequency of the waves. We have seen (Table V) that the electron concentrations in the layers increase with height; the

D-layer contains the smallest number of electrons per cubic centimetre and the F_2-layer the greatest. The waves of lowest frequency are reflected from the region of lowest electron concentration—the D-layer—and those of highest frequency are returned by the F_2-layer. Between these extremes we have the medium-wave band, such as is used for broadcast transmissions. These waves are reflected in the E-layer (Fig. 4.4). Were it not for the existence of the ionosphere all the energy radiated upwards from a transmitter would be lost into outer space and we should be compelled to rely upon the very limited range of the ground-wave for purposes of radio communication. It is this fact, of course, which restricts the usefulness of the very highest frequencies, since these penetrate all the layers and fail to return.

We have spoken of the waves being reflected from the layers, but the process is really one of refraction. The depth of the E-layer is about 40 km. and that of the F-layer is much greater. As radio waves pass upwards into a layer they encounter an increasing number of free electrons. The depth to which the waves can penetrate depends upon their frequency. With increasing frequency they travel further and further in, until eventually, as the critical frequency is reached, they pass right through the region of greatest electron concentration which is situated near the middle of the layer.

Let us suppose that the frequency is somewhat below the critical value and that the waves strike the layer at an angle of, say, 45°. That part of the wave-front which is uppermost encounters more free electrons than that which is underneath. The electrons are set in oscillation by the electrical vibrations of the waves. Each electron acts as a small radio receiver, absorbing the energy falling upon it and radiating it again in all directions. Now, theory shows that the net result of this behaviour of the electrons is to increase the velocity of propagation

—the phase velocity as it is called—while the waves are passing through the electron gas. We may think of the radio waves while they are in the ionized region as being elastic. The action of the electrons is to stretch the elastic, that is to increase the wavelength temporarily as the waves are passing through. The stretching is greatest where the electrons are most numerous. The effect is, therefore, always to bend the wave-front round in one direction—the direction *away* from the region of greatest electron concentration. Eventually, the wave-front emerges again from the layer in a downward direction on the other side of the vertical, making with it the same angle as it had on entry.

Radio waves always lose energy as a result of their encounter with an ionized region. The layer contains, not only free electrons and ions, but also many neutral molecules. The electrons, being set in vibration by the waves, collide with the molecules, handing on to them some of the energy they have acquired. So far as the waves are concerned, this energy is lost and cannot be restored to them. Weakening, or attenuation, of this nature is greatest in the lowest layers where atmospheric pressure is high and where collisions with molecules are consequently most frequent. We are all familiar with this damping-out of the wave energy by electron collisions, in so far as it influences our reception of the medium-wave broadcast programmes. During the daytime the *E*-layer reflections are so completely absorbed that the sky-wave is of little value for reception. As sunset approaches, the increasing inclination of the solar rays diminishes the intensity of the ultra-violet light reaching the layer. Electrons become less numerous, and reflection then begins to take place from a somewhat higher level where electron collisions are less frequent and where less energy is lost. Reception in daylight hours is, therefore, limited to the nearer stations which

99

lie well within the radius of the ground-wave coverage, but only a short time after sunset the sky-wave becomes sufficiently strong for good reception of distant stations which were previously quite inaudible.

The propagation of very low frequency radio has a special interest in the study of solar-terrestrial relations. Here we are concerned with waves having frequencies less than 100 Kc./s. and wavelengths longer than 3,000 metres. At these long wavelengths the ground-wave weakening is so much less than for the shorter waves that good reception can often be had at distances of the order of 1,000 km. (620 miles). The distance at which the ground-wave can be picked up depends upon many factors, such as, for example, the earth-curvature, the presence of mountains en route, and the electrical conductivity of the surface over which the waves must travel. In circumventing all these obstacles the very low frequency waves have a big advantage. Another important consequence of low frequency is this, that the sky-wave penetrates into the base of the D-layer to a distance which is small compared with the length of the waves (Fig. 4.4). This means that reflection takes place as it were from a mirror surface, and there is comparatively little attenuation of these waves due to electrons colliding with neutral molecules. What absorption there is will be less by night, when the height of reflection is somewhat greater, than by day; and for the same reason it will be less in winter than in summer.

An interesting consequence of these properties of the long waves is the following. At very considerable distances from a long-wave transmitter one can have approximate equality in strength between the ground-wave, which has come by the shortest route, and the sky-wave which has arrived by a longer path and has been reflected from the D-layer. These two waves are, therefore, in a condition to interfere, and they will add, or subtract, according as they arrive at the receiving point in phase, or out of phase, with one another.

Now, as we shall see in Chapter V, the immediate effect of a flare on the sun is to produce a flash of ultra-violet light of great suddenness. The intensity of this flash may be 5 or 10 times greater than the ultra-violet

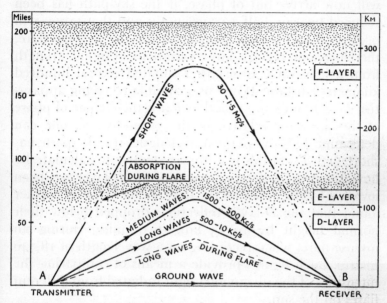

FIG. 4.4.—Normal reflections of radio waves of different frequencies from the D-, E- and F-layers of the ionosphere. During a solar flare the short waves are absorbed in the D- and E-layers and the long waves are reflected from a lower level in the D-layer.

light normally contributed from the whole of the sun's disk; and, of course, it illuminates the ionosphere only in the daylight hemisphere—where the sun is actually shining. The principal effect of the flare ultra-violet is to thicken up the electron concentration in the D-layer. So far as we have been able to ascertain its influence upon the higher layers is comparatively small. This means that the height in the D-layer, from which the waves are reflected, suddenly drops. Obviously, under these conditions the path length followed by the sky-wave between the transmitter and the receiver becomes shorter, while the ground-wave path remains unaltered. Thus, if the two waves were previously reaching the receiver in phase, so that a strong resultant signal was being heard, they will now arrive out of phase, if the sky-path has been reduced by, say, half a wavelength; and the station will become inaudible, or nearly so. During a solar flare, therefore, one records large variations in signal strength from a long-wave transmitter situated several hundred kilometres distant. If one uses suitable receiving apparatus, so as to measure exactly what is the change of phase of the sky-wave relative to the ground-wave, one can determine by how many wavelengths the sky-path has shortened. From this it is an easy matter to calculate by how much the reflecting height of the D-layer has been lowered by the action of the flare. Bracewell and Straker found that the D-layer reflections dropped below their normal height by 10–15 km. (6–9 miles) during an intense flare, when recording on a wavelength of 18,740 metres. Such figures provide a means of comparing the intensities of the ultra-violet light radiated from different flares on the sun.

The flash of flare ultra-violet light also has another effect, of a very different kind, upon the propagation of long radio waves. This is best observed at distances from the transmitter so great that the ground-wave is inaudible and the signals, therefore, arrive by D-layer reflections only. Since these reflections take place in mirror-like fashion from the bottom of the layer and the waves do not penetrate it to any great extent, an increase in ionization has the effect of improving the reflecting power of the mirror. The result is a sudden increase of signal strength at the time of the flare, and if the signals have come half-way round the world by a number of successive reflections the increase may amount to as much as 100 per cent. Many examples of these sudden enhancements are given in Chapter V, and we shall see how valuable they are as a means of recording the occurrence of flares when we cannot see the sun.

Next, let us consider some of the problems presented by the transmission of short waves. Here we have to deal with frequencies in the band 1·5 to 30 Mc./s., or wavelengths within the range 200 to 10 metres. At these high frequencies the ground-wave fades away at very short distances, so that we are concerned for practical purposes only with propagation by means of the sky-wave. This is reflected from the F_1-layer, or from the F_2-layer in the case of the highest frequencies. Such waves have their greatest importance in long-distance communication round the globe. Owing to their high frequency, energy losses due to ionospheric absorption are comparatively small under normal conditions. In order to achieve satisfactory transmissions at all times, however, it is necessary to employ the maximum usable frequency for any given distance. This must be calculated in such a way that the waves reach the receiving point by one or more reflections from the layer and so that they do not 'skip' over the receiving station. But if the frequency is too high they may penetrate the F_2-layer and be lost out into space. Consequently, in addition to knowing the distance, one must also have information of the ionospheric conditions along the great-circle path between the transmitter and receiver. These conditions vary between night and day, seasonally and with the sunspot cycle. Later we will indicate how these conditions may be forecast in advance.

We have said that the short waves suffer little ionospheric absorption under normal conditions. During a solar flare conditions become quite abnormal. The number of free electrons in the D-layer increases rapidly, and the short waves, in their passage to and from the higher F-layer, must traverse this new barrier of extra-ionization (Fig. 4.4). The result is greatly to increase the absorption at these times, so that the strength of the sky-wave signal drops to perhaps one-tenth of its previous value and is no longer audible on commercial receivers. Such 'fadeouts', as they are called, were discovered by Mögel and were later associated with flares by Dellinger. They occur so suddenly that, in the early days of radio, they were often attributed to a failure of the receiver. Many a set has been dismantled in order to ascertain the nature of the fault, before it was suspected that the ultimate cause lay in an event on the sun. Fadeouts do not occur at night; they are only experienced when the path of the waves lies partly, or wholly, within the sunlit hemisphere of the earth, and they are most severe when the channel passes through the region where the sun is overhead, that is the subsolar point. A fadeout usually lasts for about 20 minutes, and at times of great solar activity we may have as many as half-a-dozen occurring during a single day. These interruptions are, therefore, temporary and they are nothing like so serious for radio communications as another much more prolonged type of disturbance—the particle shower—which, as we shall see later, also has a solar origin.

FORECASTING IONOSPHERIC CONDITIONS

During the last twenty years a vast network of radio communications has been established linking every country of the world. The wavelengths employed are in the band 15 to 60 metres, and these short waves are transmitted by reflections from the F_2-layer. For efficient and continuous reception a knowledge of the electron population of the F_2-layer is essential. As we have seen, the number of electrons is mainly dependent upon the

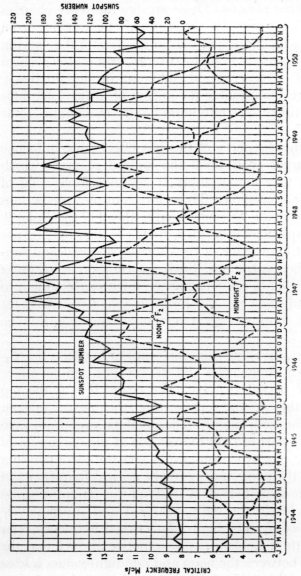

FIG. 4.5.—Mean monthly sunspot numbers and the noon and midnight F_2-layer critical frequencies during the last sunspot cycle. Reproduced from *Wireless World*, March 1951, p. 109, by courtesy of Mr. T. W. Bennington and the editors.

supply of solar ultra-violet light, and this in turn can vary for three reasons. These are (a) the daily changes in the sun's altitude, (b) the seasonal effect arising from the varying inclination of the sun's rays and the varying duration of sunlight in high latitudes, and (c) the cyclical changes of 11-year period, inherent in the sun itself, which more than double the output of ultra-violet light between times of minimum and maximum solar activity.

It was the discovery of this last effect—the influence of the sunspot cycle upon the ionized regions—which paved the way for attempts at advance forecasting of ionospheric conditions. Thus, for example, predictions can now be made for some months ahead of the F_2-layer critical frequencies for each hour of the day, making use of the past knowledge of the diurnal, seasonal and sunspot number variations. Such information is of great practical value to radio engineers; for it enables them to select in advance the maximum usable frequencies for short-wave communication over any of the long-distance channels.

In Fig. 4.5 is shown the relationship between the F_2-layer critical frequencies and the sunspot number curve during the period 1944–50. The heavy line at the top connects the points representing the mean sunspot numbers for each month. These values vary from zero in the early part of 1944 to over 200 at the maximum in May 1947. The two lower graphs give the corresponding values for the noon and midnight critical frequencies of F_2 over the same period. A study of this diagram brings out very clearly the daily, seasonal and sunspot-cycle variations of F_2. The figures for critical frequency refer to the south of England, and we notice at once that the difference between the noon and midnight values is least in summer (long days and short nights) and is greatest in winter (short days and long nights).

Now, the critical frequency is not the same thing as the maximum usable frequency which can be employed for transmissions between two distant points on the earth's surface. We recollect that the critical frequency is the frequency of waves which will just penetrate the layer in question when they are transmitted vertically upwards. But when the transmitter and receiver are far apart the waves will strike the F_2-layer at a glancing angle, as shown in Fig. 4.6, and the value of this angle of incidence i may be easily calculated when the distance D is known. The greater the value of the angle i the higher the frequency which can be reflected. The highest frequency for oblique reflection is obtained by multiplying the critical frequency for vertical reflection by the secant of angle i. For large angles, therefore, frequencies two or three times the value of the vertical critical frequency may be used for transmissions between points such as T and R in Fig. 4.6. It is necessary to keep as near as possible to the maximum usable frequencies predicted in this way; lower frequencies suffer greater absorption in the ionosphere.

Strange anomalies of radio transmission sometimes occur through these reflection effects. Police radio messages in the very high frequency band of about 45 Mc./s. (6 metres) have been received across the Atlantic. Normally these signals are restricted to a radius of a few miles by the small ground-wave coverage, and those waves which reach the F_2-layer pass right through without reflection, these frequencies being so much greater than the average vertical incidence critical frequency of about 7 Mc./s. But we see from Fig. 4.5 that, during the winter months near the time of sunspot maximum, the vertical incidence critical frequency may be as high as 14 Mc./s. This means that at such times waves which strike the F_2-layer at an angle of, say, 72°, for which sec $i = 3.24$, will be reflected, even though their frequency may be as high as 45 Mc./s. At times of sunspot minimum, when the F_2 vertical incidence critical frequency is in the region of 5 Mc./s., reflections of these very high frequencies are no longer possible.

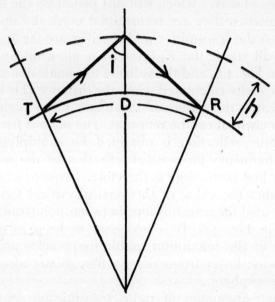

FIG. 4.6.—Calculation of maximum usable frequency for transmission between two stations T and R separated by distance D on earth's surface. If i is the angle of incidence upon the layer at height h, $f_{m.u.f.} = f_0 \times \sec i$, f_0 being the penetration frequency at vertical incidence ($i = 0°$).

These considerations emphasize the intimate connection which exists between radio communication and solar phenomena. Nevertheless, forecasts of ionospheric conditions, arrived at in this way, are liable to be upset by a number of unpredictable occurrences. In the first place, we can as yet determine in advance only the general trend of the sunspot number and of the ultraviolet light changes which accompany it. The smaller fluctuations in the sunspot number which occur from month to month are quite unpredictable. Fig. 4.5 shows that, during the maximum period of the last cycle, in the years 1947–50, there were many peaks and troughs in the curve, some lasting for six months or more and having an amplitude nearly 50 per cent of the maximum value. A drop in the number of sunspots lowers the critical frequencies.

Secondly, the F_2 critical frequencies may be greatly reduced during an ionospheric storm. These disturbances of the F-layer occur simultaneously with disturbances in the earth's magnetism—magnetic storms—and with visible displays of the aurora borealis. All three are believed to be due to the arrival in the ionosphere, or at any rate in the earth's neighbourhood, of charged particles which have been blown out from solar flares, or from other active regions in the sun. The travel time of these particles from the sun appears to be of the order of 1–2 days. Appleton and Piggott, who have investigated the influence of the particle showers upon the F_2-layer, find that the reduction of electron concentration is greatest in the polar regions, but may actually be increased near the equator. The storms have serious consequences for radio communication, especially in high latitudes, since the disturbance may last for several days during which time a radio 'black-out' occurs.

CHAPTER V

Solar Flares and their Terrestrial Effects

EXPLOSIONS ON THE SUN

WE have seen in the last chapter how the sun's ultra-violet light is responsible for the maintenance and control of the ionized regions in the earth's atmosphere. We now pass on to consider a type of catastrophic event in the sun—the solar flare—which has immediate reper-cussions on the earth.

Flares are best observed by light of the hydrogen α line with a spectrohelioscope—Hale's instrument which has contributed more than any other to the study of these remarkable phenomena occurring in the chromosphere. Seen in this way an intense flare is perhaps the most dynamic and fascinating sight in the whole heavens. Imagine a part of the sun's atmosphere 1,000 million square miles in extent—about the same as the area of a large sunspot—suddenly blazing up to ten times its normal brilliance in hydrogen light. Large flares consist of complex patterns of 'white-hot' filaments (Plates III and VI) which reach their maximum intensity five or ten minutes after their first appearance and then slowly decay during the next hour or two. Smaller flares are composed of bright patches, usually without any filamentary struc-ture. But whether large or small, flares always appear in the bright hydrogen plages associated with sunspots, being most frequent in the central regions of the groups and less so at increasing distances; beyond 100,000 km. (62,000 miles) from a spot they are rarely seen. Although the appearance of a flare is quite unpredictable, the chances of one occurring are much greater in connection with some types of sunspots than with others. The magnetically complex β- and γ-types are more prolific in this respect than the α-type. The experienced observer, who is hunting for flares, learns to recognize these flare-active spots and to concentrate his attention upon them; such a spot may produce thirty or forty flares during a single passage across the disk, whereas another spot of equal area may generate only a few, or none at all.

CLASSIFICATION AND PROPERTIES OF FLARES

Flares are classified on a visual scale of importance, from Class 1 (smallest) to Class 3 (largest), a higher 3+ category being reserved for those of exceptional area and intensity. In Table VI are listed some of the characteristics, such as the average durations, areas and intensities for flares of the different classes.

TABLE VI

Flare class	Average duration in minutes	Range of area in millionths of sun's hemisphere*	Approximate line-width of Hα in A at maximum brightness	Approximate central intensity of Hα at maximum brightness, as a fraction of the level of the continuous spectrum
1	17	100–300	2–4	0·8 –1·75
2	29	300–750	4–6	1·75–2·1
3	62	750–1200	6–8	2·1 –2·4
3+	∼ 180	> 1200	> 8	> 2·4

* 1 millionth of the sun's hemisphere = $1·17 \times 10^6$ sq. miles = $3·04 \times 10^6$ sq. kilometres.

The light emitted by a flare is confined chiefly to individual spectral lines. In the visible region of the spectrum there are the emission lines of hydrogen in the

Balmer series, $H\alpha$ (6,563 A.), $H\beta$ (4,861), etc., in order of decreasing intensity. The H (3,968) and K (3,934) lines of singly ionized calcium are comparable in strength with the hydrogen line $H\alpha$, and less intense lines arise from neutral helium, from ionized iron and from a few other metallic atoms in the chromosphere. From the presence of these lines in the visible waveband we can also infer that certain other lines in the invisible ultra-violet region of the spectrum may be unusually strong in a flare, such as the Lyman α line (1,216) of hydrogen and the helium line at 584 A. These ultra-violet lines of high energy may possibly be the radiations which affect the ionosphere during a flare, but we have, as yet, no proof that this is so.

In addition to the monochromatic radiations, the most intense flares also emit a spectrum of white light which is visible for a few minutes while the flare is at its brightest. The presence of white light is a matter of special interest, for it has enabled some of the greatest flares to be seen through an ordinary telescope when an observer happened to be watching the sun at the time. Mme M. d'Azambuja, in a note to *L'Astronomie* (1947, page 114), has given a list of all the flares known to have been observed in this way, commencing with the classic example of a 'white flare' which was recorded visually and independently, by Carrington and Hodgson on 1859 September 1. In recent years the writer has photographed this continuous spectrum during the flares of 1946 July 25, and 1949 November 19.

In the days before the invention of the spectroheliograph and spectrohelioscope, flares were also seen occasionally as a result of the bright reversals which they produced in the Fraunhofer hydrogen lines when the particular region of the sun's disk was focused upon the slit of a small spectroscope. Young says:

In a few instances the gaseous eruptions in the neighbourhood of a spot are so powerful and brilliant that, with the spectroscope, their forms can be made out on the background of the solar surface in the same way that the prominences are seen at the edge of the sun. . . . An occurrence of this kind fell under the writer's observation on September 28, 1870. A large spot showed in the spectrum of its umbra all the lines of hydrogen, magnesium, sodium and some others, reversed. Suddenly the hydrogen lines grew greatly brighter, so that, on opening the slit of the spectroscope, two immense luminous clouds could be made out, one of them nearly 130,000 miles in length, by some 20,000 in width, the other about half as long. They seemed to issue at one extremity from two points near the edge of the penumbra of the spot. After remaining visible about twenty minutes, they faded gradually away, without apparent motion.[1]

Drawings of this flare, as observed by Young, are given in Lockyer's *Solar Physics* (1874), page 588. Lockyer himself observed on several occasions what he called bright 'lozenges' superimposed upon the dark hydrogen lines of the chromosphere. When we compare his descriptions of the lozenges with modern photographs of the *Hα* line in a flare (see, for example, Plate II), there can be little doubt that he was, in fact, seeing the flare emission lines with his spectroscope. He expressed the view, however, that these bright reversals emanated from prominences, composed, as he said, of 'high-pressure bright hydrogen' which had been blown up from lower levels of the sun's atmosphere. We now know that true prominences, with few exceptions, absorb part of the hydrogen light which traverses them, so that when seen against the disk they appear darker than the chromosphere below.

THE DEVELOPMENT OF A FLARE

It is most important to be able to measure how the light of a flare flashes up and down and to time this accurately.

[1] *The Sun*, by C. A. Young (London, 1895: Kegan Paul, Trench, Trübner), p. 136.

We are then in a position to compare the course of its development with the many other effects which its radiation produces upon the earth. The development may be followed in one of two ways: since the flare is seen by the light which it radiates into the broad hydrogen line ($H\alpha$), we measure at frequent intervals either the central intensity of the line or the width of the line. In Fig. 5.1a, is shown the absorption line profile (XCY) of $H\alpha$ in the chromosphere. At a point of the sun's disk where a flare is beginning to brighten, this V-shaped trough becomes filled in, turning into an emission line (XAY) when the flare is brightest. At the same time the line-width (XY) rapidly broadens and the central intensity (AB) increases until the flare reaches its peak. The line-width is determined by setting the slit of the spectrohelioscope successively in positions 2 and 3 (Fig. 5.1a), at which wavelengths the bright emission merges into the background. The central intensity may be measured with a simple photometer, consisting of a strip of dark glass whose density increases along its length. This glass strip is moved across the field of view until the brightness of the flare is reduced to equality with that of a standard patch of light of constant brightness. A portion of the continuous spectrum just beyond the wings of the hydrogen line (brightness = 100 per cent) forms a suitable standard of comparison.

In Fig. 5.1b, we see the *development curves* which indicate how both these quantities vary with time during a typical Class 3 flare. The chief characteristic is the very sudden rise to maximum brightness, which we call the 'flash', followed by a much slower decline. In Table VI, are given the approximate values of line-width and central intensity which are recorded at the times of greatest brightness for flares of different classes.

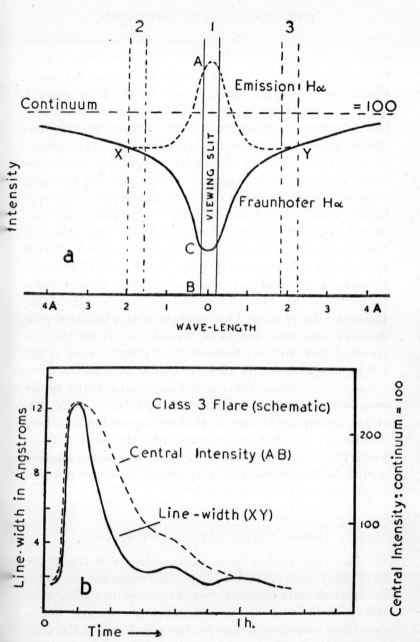

IG. 5.1.—(a) Hα emission line and (b) development curves of a solar flare.

FLARE SURGES

Flares not only emit light; they also throw out great quantities of matter from the sun. At the time when a flare is brightest, we begin to see streamers of material—like prominences, only more intense—leaving the chromosphere from the surrounding regions (Fig. 3.4*g* and *h*). Outward velocities of the order of 500 km./sec. (310 miles/sec.) are often acquired by this moving gas, and these velocities can be measured by the Doppler displacements of the spectral lines (see Plate II). When the flare occurs near the edge of the sun's disk, the appearance is that of a fountain, spewing out jets of matter to heights of half-a-million kilometres or more. In Plate VII we see a remarkable series of pictures of one of these flare prominences taken by Dr. Helen Dodson at the McMath-Hulbert Observatory. One portion of this brilliant prominence rose to a height of 50,000 km. at an average speed of 700 km./sec. Some normal prominences to the left-hand side of the pictures are almost invisible by comparison. Sometimes this ejected material returns to the sun, but more often it fades into invisibility while it is still in the coronal space, so that we can no longer follow its history. We suspect, however, that the matter we *see* forms but a small part of much larger streams of ionized, and therefore invisible, atoms which leave the sun and depart into space at these times.

TERRESTRIAL EFFECTS OF FLARES

We have found that flares emit radiation of two types, both waves and particles. In the race from the sun to the earth, both start together; but the waves, travelling with the speed of light, win by a comfortable margin. Whatever their wavelength may be, the travel time is the same for all, namely $8\frac{1}{2}$ minutes; consequently, all waves reach the earth at the same moment—the instant when we see the flare flashing up in the field of the spectrohelioscope. The particles lag behind, and arrive at various intervals

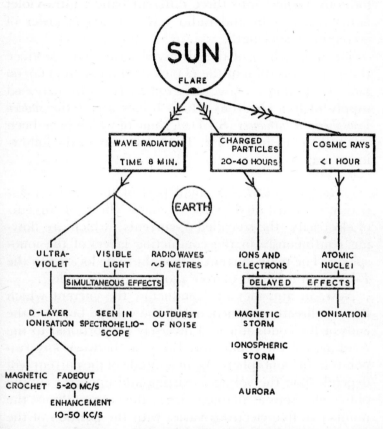

FIG. 5.2.—Terrestrial effects of solar flares.

depending upon their speeds. The waves, therefore, generate what we refer to as the *simultaneous effects* of flares; the particles give rise to *delayed effects*. With the help of the diagram in Fig. 5.2, let us consider what these effects are, and how they are produced.

SIMULTANEOUS EFFECTS

The wave radiation reaching the earth may be grouped, for convenience, into three different bands: ultra-violet light, visible light and radio waves, taken in order of increasing wavelength.

The main effect of the ultra-violet rays is to produce the extra-ionization in the D region, at a height of 60–90 km. (37–56 miles) above the ground. It is this increased supply of free electrons which brings about the *sudden ionospheric disturbances* (S.I.D.s), some of which have been referred to in Chapter IV. The S.I.D.s are of the following types:

(1) *Magnetic crochet.*—A small part of the earth's magnetism is contributed by the magnetic effects of currents of electricity (the so-called S_q-currents), which are flowing continuously in the conducting layers of the ionosphere. The main current is thought to be located in the E-layer, at a height of 100–130 km. (62–81 miles).

Now, in any metallic conductor, the current which flows is directly proportional to the voltage between the ends of the conductor and inversely proportional to the resistance of the conductor. Likewise, between any two points in the ionosphere the magnitude of the current will depend upon the voltages existing and upon the supply of free electrons available to carry the current. Since the number of free electrons varies with the position of the sun, the currents flowing overhead vary with the time of day, and so they produce the well-known diurnal variation, or swing to and fro, of the delicate magnets which record the earth's field. During an intense flare the supply of free electrons is increased; a greater current flows in the ionosphere, and the result is to generate an abrupt kick, or 'crochet' disturbance, in the records of the magnetic stations. We see these effects clearly in Fig. 5.3.

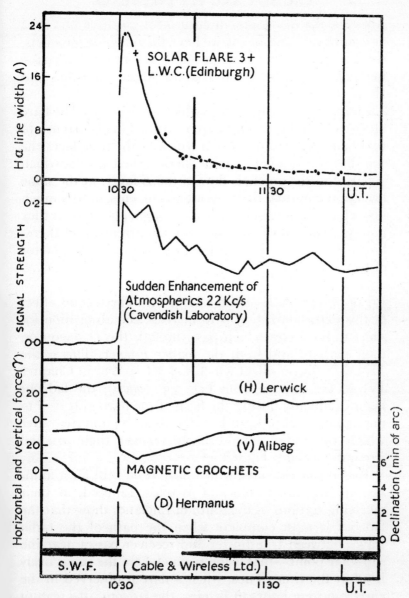

FIG. 5.3.—The development curves of a solar flare (1949 November 19) and its ionospheric effects.

Above is the development curve of a 3+ flare observed at Edinburgh, and below we have the magnetic crochets, recorded simultaneously at three stations far apart— Lerwick in the Shetland Islands, Alibag in India and Hermanus in South Africa.

Like all other disturbances which are generated by flare ultra-violet light, crochets are restricted in occurrence to that hemisphere of the earth which at the time faces the sun. But it is not yet certain whether the currents which give rise to the crochets flow in the E-layer, at the same level as the normal daily variation currents, or at a much lower level in the D-layer. If at the higher level, then they represent an increase of the normal currents, and therefore of the conductivity at the time of a flare, by a factor of two.

(2) *Short-wave radio fadeout* (*S.W.F.*).—The second effect of this extra-ionization is to increase the absorption for short radio waves which pass through the D region on their path to and from the higher F-layer. This is the Mögel-Dellinger effect which was referred to in Chapter IV. As we can see from Fig. 5.3 (*bottom*), the fadeout begins suddenly during the flash of the flare as it rises to maximum brightness; it lasts for about 25 minutes, after which the radio signals slowly recover their original strength (see also Fig. 5.6).

Records of fadeouts, which have been kept for a number of years by Cable and Wireless Limited, at their receiving stations in the south of England, show that the fadeout is most complete when the path of the radio waves between transmitter and receiver passes near the sub-solar point—that is the region where the sun is overhead at the time. Thus, when a flare is observed in the early morning hours in Britain, the fadeout affects most seriously the receptions from stations like Tokyo, Bombay and Melbourne in the eastern hemisphere; an afternoon flare, on the other hand, diminishes most strongly the signals received from New York, or Buenos Aires, in the Americas.

At these times the signal strength drops to one-fifth or one-tenth of its normal value. From this it may be inferred that the electron concentration in the D-layer increases by a factor of five or ten times during a flare; a value which is noticeably different from the increase by a factor of two derived from the crochet phenomenon. We conclude that the crochet and fadeout effects probably occur at different levels.

(3) *Sudden enhancement of atmospherics (S.E.A.)*.—When the free electrons begin to thicken up in the D region, it becomes more highly reflecting for those very long waves (about 10,000 metres wavelength) which are returned to us from near the base of the layer. If we happen to be recording the signals from a distant transmitter, there is thus an abrupt increase of signal strength. We may think of the D-layer reflecting ordinarily like a sheet of glass; during a flare it reflects like a piece of silvered glass.

Nowadays, there are few transmitters operating at these long wavelengths, and those that do are frequently 'off the air'. So it was necessary to find an alternative. We owe the alternative to Dr. R. Bureau, who thought of tuning in to the natural radio waves which are generated by the lightning flashes of thunderstorms, and who first discovered these sudden enhancements at the times of flares. Thunderstorms are in operation at all hours of the day and night, at all seasons, somewhere in the world. We are familiar with their 'crackles' and 'fizzles' on ordinary wavelengths. So all that is necessary is to build a radio set which will add up the 'crackles' of appropriate frequency, over a period of about 1 minute, and give us the result in the form of a direct current which can be registered on a moving sheet of paper. In this way we obtain a steady record of the integrated intensity of atmospherics on a given frequency for all hours of the day. When a solar flare breaks out the pen of the recorder begins to shoot up, and within a few minutes the strength of the incoming signals may have doubled.

Most of the atmospherics come to us from the tropics where thunderstorms are most numerous. The enhancements are caused simply by the improved reflecting power of the D-layer at a height of about 70 km. (44 miles); there is no question of a real increase in the number of lightning discharges at these times. Fig. 5.3 illustrates the S.E.A. recorded at Cambridge during the flare of 1949 November 19, and Fig. 5.4 shows many more examples which have been registered at Edinburgh. Almost all Class 2 and Class 3 flares occurring during the daytime are found to generate S.E.A.s. The method, therefore, forms a simple and effective means of recording and timing flares when the weather is cloudy and when the sun itself cannot be seen.

(4) *Sudden phase anomaly* (*S.P.A.*).—Not only does the *D*-layer become a better reflector for long waves during a flare, but the height of the reflecting 'ceiling' falls. In other words, the concentration of electrons necessary for reflection is found at a lower level. As explained previously, this gives rise to a change of phase between the reflected sky-wave and the ground-wave, when we are at medium distances from a long-wave transmitter and can receive both waves simultaneously. The phase anomaly effect was discovered by the Cambridge workers Budden, Ratcliffe and Wilkes, and in 1949 Bracewell and Straker found that intense flares of the $3+$ type caused phase changes of as much as $1\frac{1}{2}$ wavelengths; they were then recording at 90 km. (56 miles) distance from the Rugby transmitter which operates on a wavelength of 18,740 metres. This represents a lowering of the height

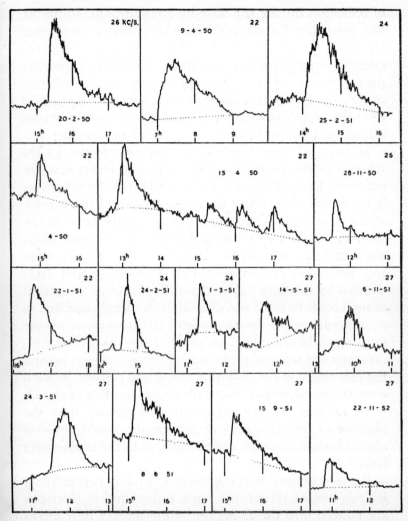

FIG. 5.4.—Sudden enhancements of radio atmospherics (S.E.A.s) caused by increased reflecting power of the *D*-layer during solar flares. Recordings made at the Royal Observatory, Edinburgh, and reproduced from the *Journal of Atmospheric and Terrestrial Physics*, **4**, 226, 1953, by courtesy of the editors.

of reflection during the flare by about 15 km. (9 miles). On the other hand, small flares of Class 1 produce a lowering of about 3 km. It appears, therefore, that the energy output of a flare in ultra-violet light is roughly proportional to its energy output in the visible radiation of $H\alpha$. We arrive at a similar conclusion from a study of the other types of sudden ionospheric disturbance considered in relation to the flares which cause them.

In 1948, when we began to time accurately the S.I.D.s relative to the flares, a rather surprising result was discovered. The maximum of the S.I.D. was found to lag behind that of the flare; the average value of the delay is about 7 minutes. Moreover, after an intense flare the D-layer did not return to normal for an hour or more after the flare had ceased to be visible in $H\alpha$ light. Since there was no reason to suppose that the ultra-violet light emitted by the flare followed a different course from that of the visible light, it was clear that this result was due to a 'sluggishness' in the response of the ionosphere to the ionizing radiation. This meant that the maximum concentration of free electrons in the D region lagged behind the maximum of the radiation which was causing it. Such a conclusion was quite contrary to the theories of the D-layer existing at the time, which supposed that the number of free electrons at this height would respond almost instantaneously to any changes in the ultra-violet light.

We now believe that the D-layer behaves rather like a leaking bucket. When the tap is turned on free electrons are poured into the D region by the flash of flare ultra-violet light as it ionizes the atoms, but all the while electrons are leaking away; and so it takes longer to fill the bucket than if there were no leaks. The leaks arise from the circumstance that while free electrons are being formed some of them are re-combining with positive ions and others possibly are attaching themselves to neutral

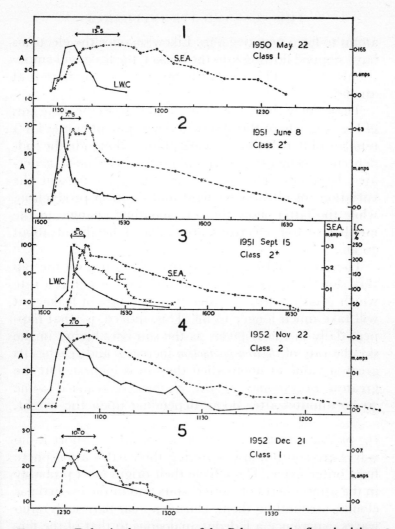

Fig. 5.5.—Delay in the response of the *D*-layer to the flare ionizing radiation. The full lines are the visually observed development curves (line-widths) of the flares (Nos. 1 and 2 were observed at Ondřejov, and 3, 4, and 5 at Edinburgh); the dashed lines represent the *D*-layer ionization, as recorded by sudden enhancements of atmospherics. In No. 3 a simultaneous plot of the central intensity (I.C.) of the flare *Hα*-line is also shown. Reproduced from the *Journal of Atmospheric and Terrestrial Physics*, **4**, 226, 1953, by courtesy of the editors.

atoms to form negative ions. Likewise, once the electrons have stopped flowing into the bucket, the leaks will empty it only slowly. This is what happens when the flare is at an end.

These delay times are clearly visible from the diagrams of Fig. 5.5, where the observed development curves for a number of flares (*full lines*) are plotted alongside the sudden enhancements of atmospherics (*dashed lines*) generated by them. The former, we believe, represent the variations of ultra-violet light and electron production, while the latter show the corresponding changes in the number of free electrons present at a height of about 70 km.

The same analogy suggests that if we turn on the tap very slowly and pour electrons into the bucket at a rate which is only a little greater than the rate of leakage it will take much longer to fill. This, indeed, is what happens daily in the *D*-layer; as the sun rises higher in the sky the rate of *electron production* increases and reaches its greatest value at noon when the sun is highest. But the greatest *concentration of free electrons* is reached some 30–60 minutes after noon, depending upon the height.

(5) *Sudden anomaly in cosmic noise* (*S.C.A.*).—Short radio waves are continuously entering the earth's atmosphere from outer space. These have their origin most probably in the atmospheres of 'active' stars and in the excited gas clouds surrounding them. During a solar flare such radio waves experience a fadeout analogous to that of the terrestrial short waves which are reflected back to us by the *F*-layer.

The ionospheric absorption of cosmic radio noise was first noticed by Jansky in 1937 and has since been studied in detail by Shain and Mitra at Sydney on a frequency of 18·3 Mc./s. It forms one of the most sensitive means of detecting the flare ultra-violet radiation (Fig. 5.6).

(6) *Radio noise burst.*—Referring again to Fig. 5.2, we see that part of the wave radiation from a flare consists of radio waves. So far we have been considering only the influence of the flare ultra-violet light upon the ionosphere; and we have noticed how these ionospheric

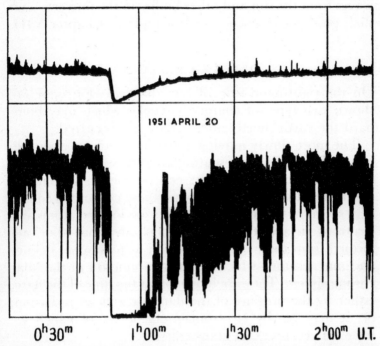

1951 APRIL 20

0^{h}30^m 1^{h}00^m 1^{h}30^m 2^{h}00^m U.T.

Fig. 5.6.—Absorption of cosmic radio noise (*above*) during a solar flare, as recorded by Shain and Mitra on a frequency of 18·3 Mc./s. Simultaneous fadeout (*below*) of short radio waves being reflected from the *F*-layer. Reproduced from *The Observatory*, **74,** 157, 1954, by courtesy of Dr. R. N. Bracewell and the editors.

changes, in turn, affect the travel of man-made radio waves between any two places on the earth's surface. But we are now confronted with something of a totally different kind; the flare itself is a transmitter of radio. The flare radio waves reach the earth from the sun at the same time as the visible and ultra-violet light which we have been discussing. They, therefore, constitute one of the simultaneous effects of flares; that is why we mention them here, along with the sudden ionospheric disturbances. Since, however, this forms part of a much wider subject—the great discovery of the emission of radio waves from the sun and other bodies in the universe—we shall postpone discussion of this topic to Chapter VIII.

DELAYED EFFECTS

On the right-hand side of our diagram (Fig. 5.2) are shown two types of charged particles which may bombard the earth shortly after a flare has occurred.

The more slowly moving particles reach us about 26 hours afterwards, representing an average speed of some 1,600 km./sec. (1,000 miles/sec.) for the whole journey. While we cannot be certain what these corpuscles consist of, it seems most probable that they are ionized atoms and electrons in about equal numbers, and that they are formed from those elements—such as hydrogen, helium and magnesium—which are most abundant in the solar chromosphere. They are blown off at the time of the flare, either by the pressure of the flare ultra-violet radiation, or, it may be, by electromagnetic forces of which we have, as yet, no exact knowledge.

On arrival in the earth's neighbourhood, they set up great currents of electricity which we can observe through their influence upon the earth's magnetism—producing the great magnetic storms. Brilliant displays of the aurora are seen in the north and south polar regions at the same time, and in exceptional cases may even extend from the poles to the equator. The aurora is nature's great 'advertising sign', giving us visual evidence that charged particles are arriving from the sun.

Wherever a flare may be located on the sun's visible hemisphere, its ultra-violet light and radio waves reach the earth, but this is not true of the showers of corpuscles. Newton, who has investigated the relationship between magnetic storms and the flares which have preceded them, finds that a magnetic storm is much more likely to follow if the flare occurs near the centre of the solar disk. This must mean that the particles leave the sun mainly in a vertical direction, just as the flare prominences are seen to do. By the same token, when a flare is located near the sun's limb the earth is less often situated in the line of particle fire.

Not every magnetic storm, or display of 'northern lights', however, has its origin in a flare; many of the lesser storms have a marked tendency to recur at intervals of 27 days—the solar rotation period—and these storms are presumed to be linked with regions on the sun which are continuously emitting streams of particles for long periods, rather like jets of water from a rotating hose which splash the earth periodically as they turn round. We shall revert to these matters when we come to consider the earth's magnetism.

The fastest particles emitted by flares are believed to be similar to primary cosmic rays. These are charged atomic particles of exceptionally high energies, travelling with speeds which are an appreciable fraction of the speed of light. Cosmic rays bombard the earth's atmosphere from all directions with remarkable constancy. Atmospheric atoms are disintegrated by these fast projectiles, and what we observe at the bottom of the atmosphere are merely the secondary effects of such atomic explosions.

The four greatest flares which have occurred during the past twelve years, since continuous records of cosmic rays began, have generated sudden increases of cosmic ray intensity. The most celebrated example was that of 1949 November 19, when the cosmic ray records at Climax (11,500 feet) showed a sudden increase of 180 per cent above normal. The maximum was reached 1 hour after the peak intensity of the flare had been recorded at Edinburgh. The implications of these cosmic ray bursts are considered more fully in Chapter IX.

WHAT ARE FLARES?

Twenty years ago we pictured the sun's atmosphere as composed of a layer of hot gas, quietly radiating into space the energy which it received from the still hotter interior. Our present picture is very different. Both the photosphere and chromosphere are seen to be in a highly turbulent state; and we find occurring in them electric and magnetic phenomena for which there are no obvious parallels on the earth.

It is clear from the remarkable train of events to which flares give rise that they are of an exceedingly complex nature, involving many branches of physics which are new and only partially explored. Let us consider the main facts which have to be explained by any theory. The most outstanding feature is the sudden flash of radiation which occurs shortly after the commencement. Some of the most rapid flares develop to peak intensity in less than one minute. This means that a region of the chromosphere several hundred million square miles in extent may increase its radiation by a factor of ten in that short time. We are tempted to suppose that a geiser of hot gas must be blown up from the sun's interior, carrying its radiation energy with it. The evidence of the flare spectrum, however, is strongly opposed to such volcanic eruption theories. In the first place, the flare emission lines show no appreciable Doppler displacements, as they would do if the radiation came from hot gases issuing outwards from inside the sun. Secondly, the spectrum is that of a *cool* gas, little, if at all, hotter than its surroundings. The atoms in a flare, therefore, radiate not because their temperature has been increased, thereby causing them to collide with one another at greater speeds, but because they are excited to emit radiation by some other mechanism. What is this mechanism?

The most attractive hypothesis is excitation by a stream of runaway electrons. Such a theory was first proposed by Giovanelli in 1948. The chromosphere contains a plentiful supply of free electrons, and it is, therefore, a good conductor of electricity. In the vicinity of a sunspot the magnetic field is changing rapidly, especially in the early stages of growth. Now, a *changing* magnetic field generates an electric field, that is to say, it produces electromotive forces in its neighbourhood. Ions and electrons will begin to flow along certain paths round the sunspot, and the electrons, being the lighter particles, may be quickly accelerated to high speeds, as they acquire energy from the field more rapidly than they lose it by collisions. Atoms which are struck by these runaway electrons also gain sufficient energy to cause them to radiate in their normal spectral lines. On this theory the flare is a 'discharge' generated by the varying magnetic field of the sunspot region. The theory gives plausible explanations of many of the observed characteristics; such as the sudden onset, the proximity to sunspots, the stationary nature of flares, their association with the central regions of magnetically complex spots and the absence of great heating of the chromospheric gases. The theory has not yet been developed along lines which would account for the ejection of particle streams and the propagation of radio noise.

Bruce has proposed the view that both prominences and flares are analogous to terrestrial lightning flashes, but occurring on a much grander scale in the solar 'thunderstorms'. There is, however, a significant difference in this respect between the chromosphere and the lower regions of the earth's atmosphere: the former is a good conductor of electricity, whereas the latter is normally an insulator. When charged droplets of opposite sign accumulate in adjacent thunderclouds, little happens until the voltages become great enough to break down the insulation between them. Ions and electrons are then formed and a violent discharge of current follows; this is accompanied by the visible radiation of the atoms along the path. Since the chromosphere is at all times a good conductor, it is difficult to understand how oppositely charged particles could accumulate on a large enough scale in near-by regions. But it is conceivable that something of this sort might happen near sunspots, where powerful magnetic fields are known to exist. Cowling and others have shown that when an ionized gas is situated in a magnetic field, and the pressure is suitable, the conductivity may be much greater along the magnetic lines of force than in a direction at right angles. It is possible under these conditions that positive ions and negative electrons might be separated out into adjacent regions and held there, until some sudden readjustment of the magnetic field allowed a discharge to flow between them. At present we are only groping towards an understanding of these electromagnetic phenomena in the sun.

STELLAR FLARES

Finally, we may ask: do flares occur on other stars? This is a difficult question to answer, because we cannot see the surfaces of stars; we can only watch their total light and study their spectral lines. The largest solar flare covers less than one-hundredth part of the sun's hemisphere and would not contribute appreciably to its output of visible light, nor in all probability could we detect its influence upon the $H\alpha$ line in the light received from the whole disk. However, we must not exclude the possibility that, among the enormous variety of stellar types, there may be stars which are much more flare-active than the sun; stars, a large part of whose surfaces may be continuously flare-producing.

Variable stars of many kinds have been known for a long time. Of those with short periods, some are binaries which vary in brightness because of periodic eclipses, others because of an inherent instability which causes the star's surface to pulsate in and out. Among the latter class are the RR Lyrae variables, whose light rises and falls regularly with a period of about one day. Only in the past few years have variable stars been discovered whose light flashes up and down in a matter of minutes, like that of a solar flare. The most celebrated example of a 'flare star' is UV Ceti. This is a dwarf red star of the 12th magnitude, one of the components of a binary star in the constellation Cetus. Its most remarkable performance took place on 1952 September 25, when its total light increased by 5 magnitudes (one hundred-fold) in 20 seconds, the record being obtained with a photoelectric cell. It has made many similar flashes, though none quite so great as this. We have no certain knowledge how these cool, red stars can flare up in this manner and then revert to their normal condition in so short a time. Pulsation cannot supply the answer. It seems most probable that we have to deal with some form of electromagnetic discharge in the star's atmosphere, similar to that which we have been discussing in relation to the sun.

Then there are stars, like those of the Wolf-Rayet type, whose spectra show immensely wide and variable emission lines. It has been suggested by Johnson that the atmospheres of these stars are in a continuous state of flare activity, so that we can see little else but the light which comes from the flare discharges and from the particles which they blow outwards.

CHAPTER VI

The Sun and the Earth's Magnetism

THE EARTH A MAGNET

WILLIAM GILBERT, physician to Queen Elizabeth I, made the earliest experimental study of the earth's magnetism. In his book *De Magnete*, published in 1600, he describes how he fashioned a magnetized sphere from a piece of naturally occurring lodestone, and demonstrated, by bringing small magnets near it, that its magnetic field was similar in form to that of the earth. It was left to Gauss and later workers to show that the earth's field approximates very closely to that of a uniformly magnetized sphere (Fig. 6.1a), but this is only true if the magnetic axis is inclined at $11\frac{1}{2}°$ to the earth's geographic axis. The magnetic axis poles are, therefore, assumed to be located at opposite ends of a diameter of the earth, in latitude 78·5° N, longitude 69° W and in latitude 78·5° S, longitude 111° E.

We can see from Fig. 6.1a that, over the greater part of the earth's surface, the direction of the earth's field is steeply inclined to the horizontal, the inclination being 90° near the axis poles and 0° at the magnetic equator. For convenience of measurement and analysis, the magnetic Force (F) at any place is resolved (Fig. 6.1b) into Vertical and Horizontal components, V and H respectively. The angle (I) between F and H is known as the Dip, and the angle (D) between the direction of H and the geographical meridian is known as the magnetic Declination.

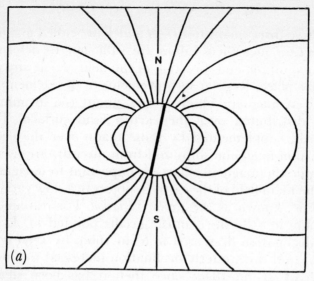

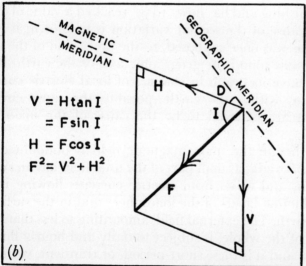

FIG. 6.1.—(a) Lines of force in the neighbourhood of
the earth, regarded as a uniformly magnetized sphere.
NS, magnetic axis; heavy line, geographic axis; (b) the
horizontal (H) and vertical (V) components of the
earth's field (F) lying in the plane of the magnetic
meridian. I is the angle of dip and D is the angle of
declination.

These three quantities D, H and V are called magnetic elements, since their values are sufficient to determine the magnitude and direction of the field (F) at any particular place. Regular measurements of the elements are made at magnetic observatories, about 100 in number, well distributed over the earth's land surface. Their records, supplemented by those made over the oceans from non-magnetic ships and from aircraft, are used to compile the magnetic charts so important to navigation.

The main field of the earth is subject to a slow variation in time, known as the *secular variation*. For example, at London in 1580 the compass needle pointed 11° E, and the declination decreased to 0° in 1660; by 1700 it was 7° W, and this westerly declination increased to a maximum of 24° in 1820; since then it has been steadily diminishing and has now (1953) reached a value of 9° W. The cause of the secular variation is unknown; it is not due, as was once supposed, to the precession of the magnetic axis round the geographic axis of the earth. But it may have its origin in changes of local electric currents flowing within the earth, possibly the same currents which are believed to be the cause of the main field itself.

Although the main magnetic field is undoubtedly of *internal* origin, a small part of the total field has an *external* origin, and arises from electric currents flowing in the conducting layers of the ionosphere and in the surface of the earth. The external field, amounting to less than 1 per cent of the whole, is subject to daily and hourly fluctuations; and it is these short-period, or transient, variations which are of the greatest interest in the study of solar-terrestrial relations.

Continuous records of the fluctuations in D, H and V are made at every magnetic observatory. The instruments used are called magnetographs. Each consists of a delicate magnetic needle, suitably suspended so as to

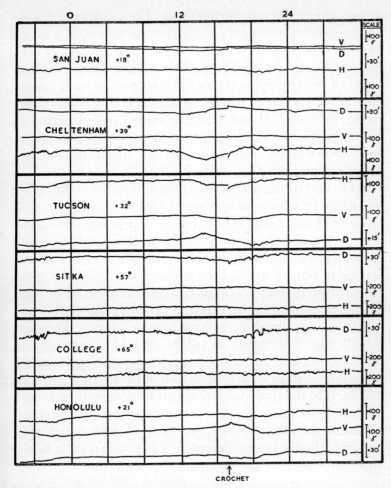

O 12 24

SCALE

SAN JUAN +18°
V
D ⌐+30′
H

CHELTENHAM +39°
D ⌐+30′
V ⌐-100
H

TUCSON +32°
H ⌐+100
V ⌐-100
D ⌐+15′

SITKA +57°
D ⌐+30′
V ⌐-200
H ⌐-200

COLLEGE +65°
D ⌐+30′
V ⌐-200
H ⌐-200

HONOLULU +21°
H ⌐+100
V ⌐+100
D ⌐+30′

↑
CROCHET

FIG. 6.2.—Magnetograms in *H*, *D* and *V* for the same day (1949 September 17) at stations in different latitudes. The *daily variation* (solar ultra-violet light effect) is most marked in middle latitudes (Tucson and Cheltenham, Md.); the *disturbance* of the traces (solar particle effect) is visible in high latitudes (College and Sitka, Alaska). A *crochet* (solar flare effect) at 17ʰ 16ᵐ affected all traces simultaneously and coincided with the observation of a Class 3 flare. Reproduced by courtesy of the Director, U.S. Coast and Geodetic Survey.

record the changes in one element. The small movements of the needles are highly magnified by means of a beam of light; the light is reflected from a mirror attached to the needle and it is then brought to a focus upon a moving sheet of photographic paper. The records of such instruments are known as magnetograms. Fig. 6.2 shows magnetograms in D, H and V for the same 24-hour period at six magnetic stations in different latitudes. Traces of this kind provide the raw materials for all studies of the transient magnetic variations.

The variations are of two main types: (a) the *daily variations*, in which each element repeats a characteristic cycle of changes that is found to be dependent upon local time and upon the latitude of the station; and (b) a disturbance, or unsteadiness, of the traces which is of an irregular nature and whose occurrence is, for the most part, unpredictable. The disturbance is greatest in high latitudes, and when it exceeds a certain rather arbitrary value it is referred to as a 'magnetic storm'. Days on which the disturbance is below normal are known as 'quiet days', and under these conditions the regular daily variation is most clearly seen and studied. In the traces of Fig. 6.2, the daily variation can be observed in D and H for Cheltenham (39° N). At College (65° N) the daily variation amplitude is less, but here we also notice that the disturbance is considerably greater, this station being so much closer to the geomagnetic north pole.

THE DAILY VARIATION

On days when the magnetic traces are fairly free from irregular disturbances the three elements undergo a cycle of changes having a 24-hour period. The form of these changes is shown in Fig. 6.3, which is typical of the latitude of the south of England during the spring and autumn months. The curve marked ΔH shows the variations [1] in the strength of the horizontal force (H), which can be seen to reach its minimum value at about 11^h (local time); the trace ΔV, showing the daily changes in V, has a minimum near noon and two small maxima at about 5 hours on either side of noon, while the trace showing the changes in D has a minimum at 8^h and a maximum at 13^h. Similar variation patterns are found

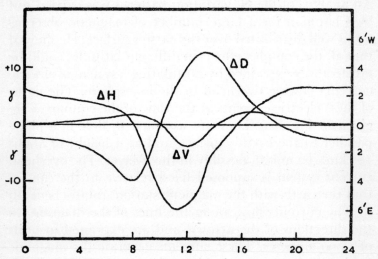

FIG. 6.3.—Mean *daily variation curves* for quiet days in the three elements, plotted against local time for the latitude of the south of England.

for magnetic stations in the same latitude; but in other latitudes both the amplitudes and the times of maxima and minima are strikingly different. These cyclical departures of the elements from their mean values are referred to as the S_q variations, S denoting that they have a solar origin and q that they are measured on magnetically quiet days. As evidence of their solar origin, we may note

---

[1] Variations in H and V are measured in terms of the unit γ, which is one hundred-thousandth part of the unit of magnetic field, one gauss. Changes in D are measured in minutes of arc. The intensity of the earth's field ranges from 0·3 gauss at the equator to 0·7 gauss at the poles.

that the amplitude of the variation in each element is dependent upon the following factors: (a) local time, (b) latitude, (c) season of the year, and (d) the year in the sunspot cycle.

OVERHEAD CURRENTS

An analysis of the S_q variation patterns was carried out by Chapman for a large number of magnetic observatories well distributed over the earth's surface. He showed that all the complex effects in different latitudes could be satisfactorily explained by postulating a system of electric currents flowing overhead in the ionosphere. The paths of these electric currents at the time of the equinoxes are given in Fig. 6.4. They are assumed to flow in a plane parallel to the earth's surface and at a height of about 100 km. (62 miles), possibly in the E-layer. The overhead current system is supposed fixed relative to the sun, so that the earth with the magnetic stations rotates beneath it. The currents flow along the lines of the diagram, in the directions of the arrows, and are expressed in units of 1,000 amperes. These currents generate the magnetic fields which on the earth's surface give rise to the S_q variations of the elements, as illustrated in Fig. 6.3. We notice that the currents are greatest in the daylight hemisphere (6^h to 18^h local time) and least in the night hemisphere (18^h to 6^h), and that the maximum current precedes the sun by about 1 hour.

By means of such a current diagram (Fig. 6.4) we can predict the general features of the S_q variation in each element at any given magnetic station whose latitude is known. A conductor of electricity possesses a magnetic field whose direction is given by the 'right-hand rule'; that is to say, if we clasp the conductor with the right hand, so that the thumb is in the direction of the current flow, the fingers indicate the direction of the magnetic lines of force which envelop the conductor. As an example, let us take the case of a station in latitude 50° N. Between 6^h and 11^h we see that the overhead current is flowing mainly in a southerly direction; during this period there will consequently be a magnetic field at the surface directed towards the east. The declination (D) needle will, therefore, experience a deflection to the east of its mean posi-

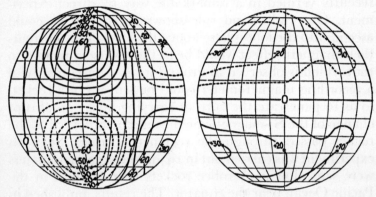

FIG. 6.4.—The overhead current systems in the ionosphere at a height of about 100 km., believed to be responsible for the solar daily variations in the earth's magnetic field. These are the conditions at the equinox during sunspot minimum. The sunlit hemisphere is on the left and the night hemisphere on the right. The earth revolves below this current system and the meridians are drawn at one-hour intervals. The currents are expressed in units of 1,000 amperes and flow in the direction of the arrows. Reproduced from *Geomagnetism*, **2,** p. 696, Fig. 1, S. Chapman and J. Bartels, by courtesy of the authors and the Oxford University Press.

tion and this will be a maximum at about 8^h, decreasing to zero at 11^h, when the direction of the overhead current becomes east–west. Between 11^h and 15^h the currents are directed mainly to the north, and during these hours the declination needle is deflected to the west of its mean position, the deflection reaching a maximum near 13^h. During the night hours, when the overhead currents are smaller, the departures of the elements from their mean values are less than during daylight (Fig. 6.3). At other seasons of the year the pattern of the overhead currents is similar to that of Fig. 6.4, though the current strengths vary and the pattern also moves north or south in latitude depending upon the position of the sun.

The existence of the overhead current system remained a pure hypothesis for many years, until its presence was recently verified in a remarkable way by direct experiment. Our right-hand rule shows us that if we could ascend into the ionosphere above the level of the currents their magnetic effect would be in the reverse direction to that which is observed at ground level. Consequently, if a recording magnetometer could be sent up in a rocket, so as to penetrate the current carrying layer, an abrupt change of the S_q-magnetic field would be observed as the rocket passed through the region concerned. Such an experiment was carried out in 1949, when magnetometers were sent aloft in Aerobee rockets from a point in the Pacific Ocean near the equator. The results, published in 1951 by Singer, Maple and Bowen, clearly established the existence of overhead currents in a layer between 93 and 105 km. above the earth.

THEORIES OF THE OVERHEAD CURRENTS

What is the mechanism by which the sun can maintain and control currents of the order of 50,000 amperes flowing in the E-layer? The first clue to the mystery is to be found in the close association between the mean amplitude of the daily variation and the sunspot cycle. This has been expressed by Wolf for different latitudes in the form

$$\Delta D = 6'\cdot 67 + 0\cdot 039R \text{ (Greenwich)}$$

where ΔD is the range of the annual mean daily variation in declination and R is the Zürich sunspot number. This shows that at Greenwich, for example, the mean daily range in declination is 6·67 minutes of arc when there are no sunspots ($R = 0$) and that at an average sunspot maximum ($R = 100$) it may increase by about 50 per cent. This means that the overhead currents, which generate the S_q-field, must vary in like proportion.

Now, as we have seen, the radio experiments of Appleton and Naismith led to the conclusion that the number of free electrons in the E-layer varied with the number of sunspots, being about 50 per cent greater in years of many spots than in years when there were few spots. Consequently, there is a strong presumption that the magnitude of the overhead current system is controlled mainly by the number of free electrons available in the E-layer to carry the current, this number being determined by the intensity of the sun's ultra-violet light. But, while ions and electrons are essential to carry the current, they cannot maintain it; electromotive forces between different parts of the ionosphere are required to do this.

A theory to account for the S_q variation and the atmospheric current system was proposed by Balfour Stewart as far back as 1882. An essential part of his theory was the suggestion that there existed a conducting layer in the upper atmosphere—and this was 20 years before the radio experimenters came to realize that such a conductor was needed to reflect their waves back to the ground. Stewart believed that the overhead currents were generated by convection of the upper air through solar heating. The conducting air, rising by convection, cuts across the earth's permanent magnetic field and electromotive forces are established. This has been called the atmospheric *dynamo* theory; and the analogy is appropriate, since the earth's field acts as the magnet and the conducting air takes the place of the moving coils in the armature. Stewart ascribed the larger S_q variation at the time of sunspot maximum to enhanced solar heating and stronger convection currents, but this view never met with general acceptance. More free electrons leading to improved conductivity is the most probable cause of the greater overhead currents when the sunspot number is high. The dynamo theory was developed mathematically by Schuster, and later by Chapman in a form which also accounts satisfactorily for the much smaller lunar daily variation (L), attributable to the tidal action of the moon upon the upper atmosphere.

MAGNETIC CROCHETS

The crochet [1] has been referred to previously as one of the simultaneous effects of an intense solar flare. Crochets are transient disturbances of small amplitude, say 30γ in H and V or $5'$ in D, occurring in the continuous records of the three elements H, D and V (see Figs. 6.2 and 5.3). The duration of the crochet is comparable with the life of the flare as seen in the spectrohelioscope, but its duration is, on the average, less than that of the other types of sudden ionospheric disturbance.

The restriction of the crochet to the sunlit hemisphere and its simultaneity with the flare which generates it prove that we have to deal with an effect of ultra-violet light. We have seen that the magnitude of the overhead current in the E-layer is most probably determined by the number of free electrons present. The burst of flare ultra-violet suddenly increases the electron population and allows a greater current to flow. If this explanation is correct then a simple conclusion follows; the direction of the crochet impulse on the magnetograms should be in the same sense as the daily variation departure existing in that element at the time. This was put to the test by McNish, who examined the crochets occurring over a whole hemisphere at the times of three flares in 1936. He

[1] Derived from the French 'crochet magnétique'.

verified that their directions and magnitudes could be satisfactorily explained on the assumption that they were generated by a sudden augmentation of the S_q currents then existing over each magnetic station. These results have since been verified by Newton and by McIntosh.

However, the location in height of the crochet currents is still open to doubt. Do they flow in the E-layer at a height of about 100 km., which is the level of the S_q currents, or do they flow, as the writer has suggested, at a much lower level between 60 and 70 km.? The electromotive forces presumably exist over a considerable range of height, and the crochet currents will circulate at whatever height sufficient electrons are formed to carry them. If at the higher level, we have to explain why it is that crochets only occur during intense flares of Class 2 rating and above. We know that the ultra-violet light from a Class 1 flare penetrates down to the D region at 75 km., so it must also pass through E at 100 km., but it generates no crochet. Crochets are only recorded when we obtain deep ionization of the D-layer down to the region of 60 km., as indicated by the S.P.A. and S.E.A. effects. It may eventually become possible to decide this point by launching a rocket with magnetometers at the time of a flare and crochet.

MAGNETIC DISTURBANCE—SOLAR PARTICLE EFFECT

The magnetograms at any observatory show on some days smooth and regular changes; on others they are unsteady or disturbed. It is usual to apply a figure, 0, 1 or 2, to denote the observed degree of unsteadiness; the figure 1 indicates a normal day, the figure 0 represents a day that is quieter, and figure 2 one that is more disturbed, than the normal. When these daily ratings are averaged for all the magnetic observatories, the resulting figure is known as the *international character figure* (**C**). Its value, which lies between 0·0 and 2·0, serves to distinguish between magnetically quiet days and *disturbed* days.

An improved method of expressing the degree of disturbance is by means of the **K** indices. These effectively measure for each observatory the range of the most disturbed element in each 3-hour period of the Greenwich day, the previously mentioned effects of diurnal variation having been removed. The indices range from 0—no departure from the quiet day variation—to 9, recorded only in the greatest magnetic storms.

The range of magnetic disturbance is greater in high than in low latitudes, and it is greatest in two belts which encircle the magnetic poles at distances of about 23° from each. As we shall see later, these are also the regions where displays of the aurora are most frequent. As an example of the manner in which the degree of disturbance increases towards the auroral zone, the ranges attained during a typical large storm at Abinger, Eskdalemuir and Lerwick, geomagnetic latitudes respectively, 54·0°, 58·5° and 62·5°, are in the approximate ratio 1 : 2 : 4. This variation of disturbance with latitude is allowed for in the scaling of the **K** indices by the selection, once and for all at each observatory, of range limits such that the frequencies of occurrence of **K** indices 0, 1, 2, etc., are approximately equal for all observatories. The **K** indices are then combined for a number of selected and widely distributed observatories into planetary ($\mathbf{K}_p$) indices, which are designed to measure the general geomagnetic disturbance over the earth in each 3-hour period.

A remarkable parallelism exists between the average degree of disturbance and the sunspot numbers. This correspondence is shown in Fig. 6.5, where the mean values of the unsteadiness (**U**), based upon the day-to-

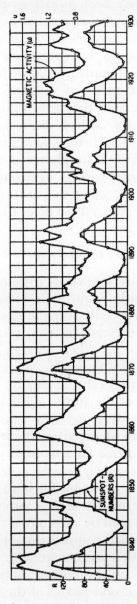

FIG. 6.5.—Relationship between annual means of magnetic activity (**U**) and relative sunspot numbers (**R**), 1835–1930 (J. Bartels). Reproduced from *Terrestrial Magnetism and Atmospheric Electricity*, **37**, 1, 1932, by courtesy of the editors and Prof. J. Bartels.

day variability of H, have been plotted by Bartels against the Zürich sunspot numbers over the period 1835–1930. Here we have one of the most clearly established of solar-terrestrial relationships, the interpretation of which has occupied the attention of many geophysicists. It has long been realized that the cause of magnetic disturbance must be very different from that which gives rise to the other transient variations we have been discussing. Unlike the crochet effect, the disturbances are observed in both the sunlit and dark hemispheres of the earth. In view of these facts, most workers in geomagnetism are now in agreement in ascribing the disturbance phenomena to the arrival of charged particles from the sun.

MAGNETIC STORMS

Intense disturbances are known as *magnetic storms*. The greater storms frequently begin with a *sudden commencement* which is simultaneous all over the world. Although there is much variety in detail, the storm traces show the same characteristic features, wherever they are recorded. In the traces of horizontal force (H), there is usually an increase above the normal value lasting for several hours during the first phase of the storm (see Fig. 6.6); this is quickly followed by a decrease to a value well below normal during the main phase, after which comes a slow recovery that may continue for several days. The storm disturbance is relatively much greater in H than in D or V, and it is in the same direction for both the northern and southern hemispheres. These facts imply that at such times the earth is enveloped by an external magnetic field whose lines of force coincide approximately in direction with the axis of the earth's permanent field. The direction of this external field must undergo a quick reversal between the first and second phases of the storm.

Magnetic storms are divided, somewhat arbitrarily,

148

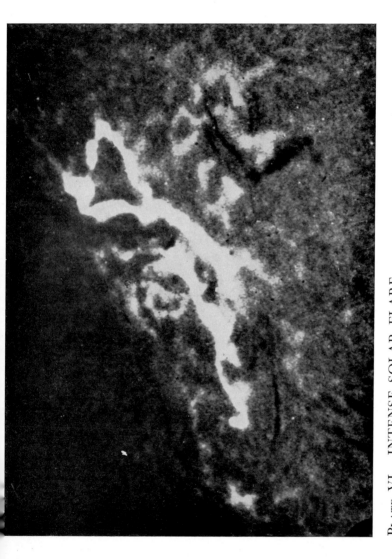

PLATE VI.—INTENSE SOLAR FLARE

Photographed in *Hα* light by Prof. T. Royds at Kodaikanal Observatory on 1926 February 22. (*Reproduced by courtesy of Prof. Royds.*)

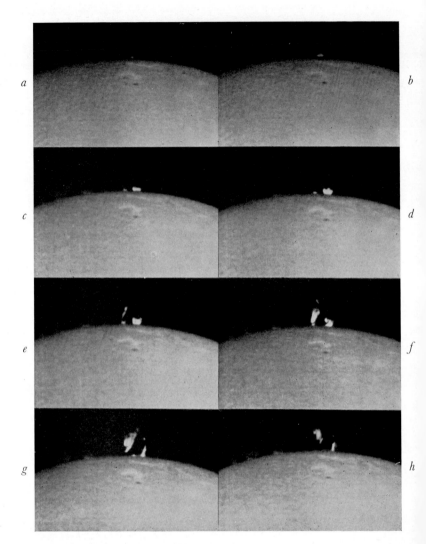

PLATE VII.—FLARE PROMINENCE

A brilliant prominence being blown out from a flare at the sun's limb. Photographs taken in $H\alpha$ light at the McMath-Hulbert Observatory on 1951 May 8, under the supervision of Dr. Helen W. Dodson. Times are as follows: (*a*) 1500·7 U.T.; (*b*) 1503·5; (*c*) 1505·2; (*d*) 1505·7; (*e*) 1506·3; (*f*) 1507·4; (*g*) 1510·0 and (*h*) 1511·9. A prominence of normal intensity appears to the left, and on the disk a plage area and sunspot can be seen. (*Reproduced by courtesy of Dr. Dodson.*)

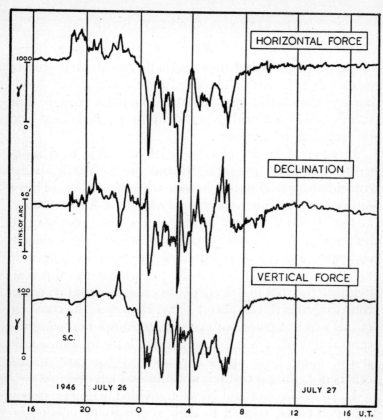

FIG. 6.6.—Great magnetic storm starting with sudden commencement (S.C.). The S.C. followed 26 hours after the great solar flare
of 1946 July 25 (see Plate III and Fig. 8.6). Magnetograms recorded
at Eskdalemuir Observatory, Scotland, and reproduced by courtesy
of the Director, Meteorological Office, Air Ministry.

into two classes—great storms and small storms—according to the magnitude of the disturbance. At Abinger, in
the south of England, the limits are taken as:

Great storms $\geqslant$ 300γ in H or V, or 60′ in D,
Small storms $\geqslant$ 150γ in H or V, or 30′ in D.

THEORIES OF MAGNETIC STORMS

Shortly after Thomson's discovery of the electron, Birkeland (1896) proposed that magnetic storms were due to beams of these particles issuing from the sun and descending into the earth's atmosphere in the polar regions. The theory was developed experimentally by Birkeland and theoretically by Størmer.

In 1904 Maunder of Greenwich was able to demonstrate that great magnetic storms on the earth always coincided approximately in time with the passage of large sunspots across the sun's central meridian. More exactly, he found that the storm began, on the average, about 26 hours after the central meridian passage of the sunspot, corresponding to a position of the spot in longitude 14° W. This suggested that the particle stream was issuing from the spot in a vertical direction and that its travel time to the earth was about 1 day. However, the converse of this was not true: not every large sunspot crossing the central meridian was followed a day later by a magnetic storm. Some large spots appeared to generate storms, others not; the precise relationship was left obscure.

In 1928 Greaves and Newton divided magnetic storms into two types, related to their geomagnetic effects: (a) mostly great storms whose occurrence showed a close dependence upon the central meridian passage of large sunspots, and (b) lesser storms, apparently unassociated with sunspots, but which showed a marked tendency to recur at 27-day intervals. At about the same time Hale spectrohelioscopes were established at a number of observatories and the systematic study of the chromosphere and the recording of solar flares was begun. During the maximum period of solar activity in 1936–38 it became clear that something like a one-to-one relationship existed between great storms and intense flares which had occurred near the centre of the solar disk. In 1944 Newton examined this relationship in detail. He pointed out that great storms and intense flares were both infrequent occurrences. He considered 28 cases of intense flares which had been observed in the central zone of $\pm 45°$ from the sun's central meridian. The calculated probability that a great storm should follow by chance within 2 days of one of these flares led to the result that no more than *one* such coincidence was to be expected. In fact, 17 coincidences were found among the 28 cases. This made it fairly certain that the statistical relationship which Maunder had discovered between large sunspots and magnetic storms was, in fact, one between flares and magnetic storms; if the sunspot did not happen to generate an intense flare near the time of its central meridian passage, then no storm would follow.

Newton next investigated the distribution of intense flares over the sun's disk prior to great storms, each flare being regarded as a source-point for the corpuscular emission. Dividing the flares into 'central zone' $(0°–45°)$ and 'outer zone' $(45°–90°)$, he found a much closer association between central zone flares and magnetic storms than was the case for those in the outer zone. From this it could be inferred that the blast of particles blown away from the flare region was confined within a cone-shaped beam about the vertical and that few particles were emitted from the flare in a horizontal direction. The vertical angle of the cone must be about 90°. The arrival of this blast of corpuscles some 26 hours later, reaching the earth in a 'head-on' encounter, is now considered to be the cause of the great magnetic storm with its incidental auroral effects (see Fig. 6.7a). The time interval (storm begins *minus* flare first observed) was found to be 25·7 hours from all great storms; but the five largest great storms gave a time interval of 20·3 hours.

However, we cannot ascribe all magnetic storms to particles blown out by flares. Neither great storms nor intense flares show any tendency to recur at regular intervals. But many small storms do recur at intervals of 27 days, returning regularly for periods of 6–12 months,

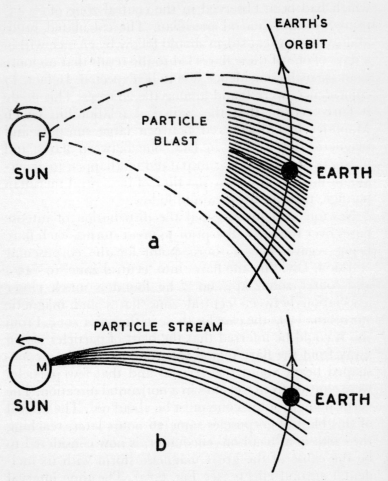

FIG. 6.7.—(*a*) Blast of particles from a solar flare meeting the earth in a head-on encounter, believed to be the cause of the great magnetic storm following 1 day after the flare; (*b*) Long-lived particle stream issuing from a solar M-region. The stream overtakes the earth in its orbit at 27-day intervals, giving rise to recurrent magnetic storms of lesser intensity.

and this peculiarity is most in evidence during the years of minimum sunspot activity when bright flares are never observed. To account for such storm sequences we have to assume the existence, not of isolated blasts of particles, but of continuous streams emitted from active regions—the so-called M-regions—of the solar surface. These solar jets, sweeping round as the sun rotates, will overtake the earth monthly in its orbit (Fig. 6.7b) for as long as the jet continues to stream outwards into space.

Of what nature are these particles and how do they generate the characteristic magnetic storm disturbances? Lindemann in 1919 pointed out that the particles could not be all of one sign, as the earlier corpuscular theories had assumed, for in that case they would repel one another and would disperse rapidly in all directions. Thus we now think of a particle stream which is composed of about equal numbers of electrons and positive ions, so that it is electrostatically neutral.

The theory advanced in 1931 by Chapman and Ferraro is the most modern of the corpuscular theories. The authors begin by considering what will happen in one of these neutral ionized streams as it is about to encounter the earth. The stream is an electric conductor; and so, when it approaches and begins to cut through the lines of force of the earth's magnetic field, electric currents will be generated within the particle cloud. These currents must be in such a direction as to *oppose* the motion, and their effect is to carve out a hollow in the approaching face of the stream. As the stream advances further, the hollow begins to envelop the earth (Fig. 6.8a), and in so doing it compresses the lines of force and, therefore, strengthens the earth's field, which, as we have seen, is the main effect observed during the first phase of a storm. At this stage the presence of the earth's field will cause positive ions to collect on the surface of the stream opposite the a.m. hemisphere of the earth and electrons opposite the p.m. hemisphere. By this time the earth is well 'into the bag', which still remains open on the night side (Fig. 6.8*b*), and the charges of opposite sign, attracting one another across the neck of the bag, begin to jump the gap. This establishes a ring of current encircling the earth (Fig. 6.8*c*), the positive ions flowing clockwise and the electrons anti-clockwise, as seen from above the earth's north pole. The current in such a ring is likely to

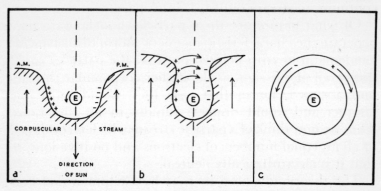

FIG. 6.8.—Chapman-Ferraro theory. Three stages in the production of a magnetic storm: (*a*) corpuscular stream of positive and negative particles approaches the earth, and a hollow is carved out by repulsion between earth's field and currents induced in the stream; (*b*) positive ions begin to leap the gap as the earth is enveloped; (*c*) a 'ring-current' circulates at a distance of several earth radii, the main stream having passed on.

flow for many days after the particles in the main stream have passed on, and it will gradually decrease in intensity as the ions and electrons re-combine. The essential feature of this circular current is that it produces at the centre of the ring (where the earth is placed) a uniform magnetic field whose direction is opposite to the main field of the earth. Consequently, the earth's field is effectively weakened during this period which constitutes the main phase of the storm. As the current dies away the field returns to normal.

Such is a very inadequate sketch of a remarkable theory. It was originally proposed to account for magnetic storms of the type which are assumed to be generated by a continuous jet-stream of narrow dimensions issuing from the sun (Fig. 6.7b). But with little modification it will also be applicable to the kind of storm that arises from a short-lived blast of particles emitted during a solar flare.

THE OBSERVATIONAL SEARCH FOR CORPUSCULAR STREAMS

However elegant and plausible the Chapman-Ferraro theory may be, as a means whereby storms *might* be produced, it will remain open to doubt whether they are, in fact, caused in this way, so long as we are unable to detect the storm producing particles by some independent means during their passage from sun to earth. Chapman himself has suggested many possible ways of attacking this problem. For example, we might try to observe the spectrum of sunlight at a time when the earth was enveloped in a particle stream. If the stream contained a sufficient number of ionized atoms of calcium, detectable amounts of sunlight might be absorbed at the characteristic frequencies of these atoms; namely, the H and K lines which appear in the violet end of the spectrum (see Plate II). But these absorbing atoms will be approaching the earth at a speed of the order of 1,600 km./sec. Consequently, such lines may be expected to show up, not at their normal wavelengths, but displaced by the Doppler effect some 20 angstroms to the violet side of their normal positions.

Here was a splendid opportunity for experiment, but an experiment of a most difficult kind, because it was certain that such absorption effects could only be small. The chance was first seized by Richardson at Mt. Wilson, who photographed the solar spectrum in the region of the calcium lines during the great magnetic storms which occurred in 1941 September and 1942 March, both following upon intense flares. Similar spectra were obtained for comparison at times when no magnetic storm particles were about. Absorption bands were found on the 'storm' plates nearly in the expected places, but so weak as to reduce the spectral brightness by no more than 1 per cent. Rather similar results were obtained a few years later by Brück and Rutllant at Cambridge.

These findings must be treated with great caution; for, as the authors themselves readily admit, the measurements are most difficult to make, and a 1 per cent variation of brightness is close to the limit of what can be detected by photographic means. Moreover, it now seems probable that the most favourable period for detecting such absorption bands would be during, or shortly after a flare has occurred, before the issuing stream of particles has had time to thin out. Kahn has shown that if the calcium atoms in the stream are capable of producing a 1 per cent absorption at the time when they are already enveloping the earth, we should expect them to produce a complete black-out in this region of the spectrum shortly after the flare, when they would be so much more highly concentrated. Nothing of the kind has ever been observed.

Since hydrogen is by far the most abundant element in the chromosphere, it is natural to seek evidence for the expulsion of hydrogen atoms during a flare. We have already referred to the punching out of high-speed surge prominences. Although the hydrogen lines of these prominences are shifted many angstroms away from their normal positions by the Doppler effect of their motion (Plate II), they are easily kept in view with the spectro-helioscope whose line-shifter is specially designed for the purpose. They move out in specific directions and much

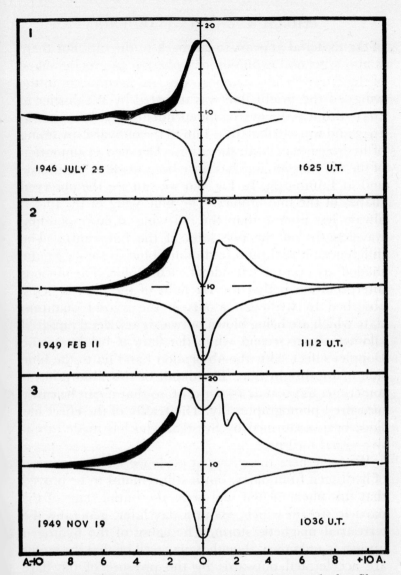

FIG. 6.9.—*H*α emission lines of intense flares photographed at Sherborne and Edinburgh. The shaded area represents the intensity difference between the blue wing of the line (*left*) and the red wing (*right*). The absorption is believed to arise from hydrogen atoms which are being expelled from the flare, possibly the initial stage of the particle blast which later generates the terrestrial magnetic storm.

of the material appears to fall back to the sun. But there is also a general expulsion of hydrogen gas, as the shape of the *bright Hα* line demonstrates. An asymmetry in the wings of the bright line was reported by Waldmeier in 1941; this was discovered independently by the writer in 1943 and was attributed by him to the outward streaming of hydrogen gas in all directions. Detailed examination of the *Hα* emission line has since been made at Sherborne and at Edinburgh. In Fig. 6.9 we can see the observed shapes of the line profiles. The blue wing of the line is always less intense than the red wing at corresponding wavelengths on the two sides of the line centre. The difference in brightness (red minus blue) is shown by the shaded area on the left side of each profile. The obvious interpretation is that the *Hα* light of the flare is being absorbed by hydrogen atoms in the second quantum state which are being blown outwards at several hundred kilometres per second while the flare is brightest: the Doppler effect shifts the absorption band on to the blue side of the bright line. The depth of this absorption is sometimes as great as 15 per cent, so that it can be easily measured photographically. The reality of the effect has since been confirmed by Švestka, who has made extensive visual measures.

We have here the strongest evidence for the emission of hydrogen from flares; but it still remains to be proved that this phenomenon represents the initial stage of the particle stream which, about a day later, generates the terrestrial magnetic storm. The cause of the hydrogen uprush is unknown, though it may well be that the atoms are accelerated outwards by the pressure of the flare ultra-violet light in the Lyman α line (1,216 A.), as was first suggested by Kiepenheuer.

Attempts have also been made to direct short radio waves on to the corpuscular streams out in space, in the hope of obtaining reflected signals after a delay of a few seconds. So far no echoes of this kind have been recorded.

In the absence of any certain confirmation of the existence of the particle streams, various alternative theories of magnetic storms have been proposed. In that of Hulbert and Maris (1929) it is supposed that the charged particles do not originate in the sun, but are formed by ionization of atoms high in the earth's atmosphere; the cause of the ionization is a burst of ultra-violet light from the sun. The subsequent movements of these ions in the atmosphere are supposed to generate the magnetic storm disturbances. The theory meets with serious difficulties in connection with such features as the time lag of about 26 hours between flare and storm, and in the 27-day recurrences of the 'M-storms'.

THE SEARCH FOR SOLAR M-REGIONS

The tendency for certain magnetic storms to recur at intervals of 27, 54, 81 days, etc., was made clear by Maunder (1904). By the use of the international character figures for denoting magnetically 'quiet' and 'disturbed' days, Chree and Stagg (1928) found that these also exhibited a striking recurrence tendency. Such results have always been taken as evidence for the existence of 'magnetically effective' regions on the sun, termed *M-regions* by Bartels. The M-regions are generally assumed to be the source points of long-lived particle streams which share in the solar rotation and which impinge upon the earth periodically in the way we have described.

If this distinction between two contrasting types of magnetic storm is correct—the recurrent type arising from long-lived particle streams originating in M-regions, and the non-recurrent type arising from isolated blasts of flare particles—we should expect to find some evidence of it in the shapes of the magnetogram records. Recent examination of the problem by the Thelliers, and by Newton, shows that this is so: they find that the recurrent storms are characterized by moderate intensity and gradual onset, whereas the flare storms are usually of greater intensity and begin with a *sudden commencement*.

Many attempts have been made to identify the hypothetical M-regions with visible solar features having a long life-time. Waldmeier (1942) found that regions of the corona which showed high intensity in the emission line 5,303 A. ('C-regions') when they appeared at the sun's east limb were often followed by terrestrial magnetic activity about 7 days later, by which time the C-regions would be located near the centre of the sun's disk. But Shapley and Roberts obtained quite a different result from coronal observations made some years later. Wulf and Nicholson (1948) have found a relationship between recurrent periods of magnetic activity and the successive appearances at the east limb of hydrogen and calcium plages; these plages are associated with sunspots but also outlive the spots by many months. They suggest that such regions emit an abnormal amount of ultra-violet light, and this, they believe, is the main agent in stimulating terrestrial magnetic activity. However, it is not clear why such activity is of only a few days' duration and does not continue during the whole fortnight while these plage areas are passing across the face of the sun.

Allen (1944), and later von Klüber (1952), have proposed the view that the white coronal streamers (visible only during total eclipses) may represent the trajectories of corpuscular streams.

However, all such relationships are based, as yet, on insufficient data; parallel records of magnetic and solar phenomena extending over many years will be needed before we can hope to reach finality in this difficult question of the particle streams and their origin.

CHAPTER VII

The Aurora

HISTORICAL

UNLIKE magnetic phenomena, which reveal themselves only to delicate instruments, displays of the aurora are visible to the world at large. Their rare and unexpected occurrences; their weird movements and flashing colours; and the total inability of the learned to account for them, have all conspired in past ages to place aurorae high up on the list of terrifying prodigies.

There is a fascinating literature dealing with these apparitions; much of it has been sifted by Fritz,[1] and still more remains to be examined. We find some of the earliest references in Aristotle [2] (fourth century B.C.). In the reign of Tiberius (A.D. 14–37) many brilliant displays were seen from Rome. Seneca describes [3] how one night, a blood-red glow being observed in the west, the Roman cohorts were despatched to Ostia to help extinguish the flames, everyone believing that seaport town at the mouth of the Tiber to be on fire. Seneca's descriptions of the common auroral forms are exceedingly clear and scientific, without any superstitious flavour.

During the middle ages we find frequent references to similar displays, variously described as 'fire-beams' and as 'burning spears' in the sky. At this period there was no clear distinction in the popular mind between aurorae

---

[1] *Das Polarlicht,* by Hermann Fritz (Leipzig 1881: Brockhaus).
[2] Aristotle, *Meteorologica.*   [3] *Naturales Questiones* I.

and comets. Natural phenomena that are recurrent and predictable produce little impact upon primitive peoples; but great comets and aurorae, appearing irregularly and at long intervals, were regarded as portents of the destruction of the world and of the end of the human race. The rare woodcut, which is reproduced in Plate VIII, illustrates an aurora that was widely seen over central Europe on 1570 January 12. The description in the legend attached to this broadsheet may be translated as follows:

In the year 1570, the 12th of January, for four hours in the night between midnight and sunrise, the portent appeared in the heavens after this fashion. At first a very black cloud went forth, like a great mountain in which several stars showed themselves, and over the black cloud was a very bright streak of light, burning like sulphur and in the shape of a ship; standing up from this were many burning torches like tapers and among these stood two great pillars, one towards the east and the other due north, so that the town appeared illuminated as if it were ablaze, the fire running down the two pillars from the clouds above like drops of blood. And in order that this miraculous sign from God might be seen by the people, the night-watchmen on the towers sounded the alarm bells; and when the people saw it they were horrified and said that no such gruesome spectacle had been seen or heard of within living memory. . . . Wherefore, dear Christians, take such terrible portents to heart and diligently pray to God, that he will soften his punishments and bring us back into his favour, so that we may await with calm the future of our souls and salvation. Amen.

(PRINTED IN AUGSBURG BY MICHAEL MANGER)

Many bright displays were also seen in England at about this time; those occurring on the nights of 1574 November 14 and 15 being sufficiently notable to attract the attention of the annalists Camden and Stow. After another active period in the 1620's there followed a century in which few aurorae were visible from Europe, so much so that the memory of these portents almost passed away. Consequently, people were taken quite unawares by the appearance of the splendid aurora of 1716 March 6 (O.S.), and much consternation ensued; for, even the scientific men of those days, such as Halley, had never seen an aurora before.

Halley's own account of this phenomenon, as given in the *Philosophical Transactions of the Royal Society*,[1] deserves to be studied by all who are interested in the history of the subject. He begins with a description of the arches, vertical rays and a brilliant corona in the zenith, as they were observed from different places in the British Isles; he refers to some earlier appearances including the display of 1621 September 2, which is described by Gassendi in his *Physicks* and where the term *aurora borealis* is used for the first time; and he proceeds to give his own interpretation of the causes. Halley dismisses with sound reasoning the notions which were then prevalent, in terms of sulphurous vapours emitted from the earth's interior, and develops the surprisingly modern view that aurorae are caused by 'magnetical effluvia' (electrical discharges, shall we say?) which are constrained to move along the lines of force of the earth's magnetic field.[2]

Wolf, who collected reports of this aurora from all over

[1] *Phil. Trans.*, 1716, p. 406. '*An Account of the late surprising Appearance of the* Lights *seen in the* Air, *on the sixth of* March *last; with an Attempt to explain the Principal* Phaenomena *thereof; As it was laid before the* Royal Society *by* Edmund Halley, J. V. D. Savilian *Professor* of Geom. Oxon, and Reg. Soc. Secr.'

[2] Needless to say, Halley's discussion of causes failed to convince the believers in prodigies, as is evident from the contents of a curiously interesting tract published soon afterwards, entitled: 'An ESSAY concerning the late APPARITION in the HEAVENS on the sixth of *March*. Proving by *Mathematical, Logical* and *Moral* ARGUMENTS, that it cou'd not have been produced meerly by the ordinary Course of NATURE, but must of necessity be a PRODIGY. Humbly offer'd to the Consideration of the ROYAL SOCIETY. LONDON: Printed for J. Morphew near Stationers Hall. 1716.'

Europe,[1] made the first attempt to measure its height above the earth. He found the altitude greater than 8 German miles (about 45 km.), but his calculation was based on the erroneous assumption that the same part of the aurora was seen from both London and Königsberg.

Aurorae visible in low latitudes occur only at times of great sunspot activity; thus we have a means of tracing back the 11-year sunspot cycle through the appearances of the aurora in Europe during the past 2,000 years. Fritz finds evidence not only for the 11-year period but of longer cycles, including one of 55 years, representing the recurrence of sunspot maxima—or a series of maxima —with activity much above the average. These long-period cycles derive some support from the sunspot numbers which have been accurately recorded during the past 200 years. Since 1750 we have had three periods of unusually intense activity, centred upon the years 1780, 1870 and 1947, with intervals in between when the 11-year maxima were correspondingly below the average.

THE AURORAL FORMS

The luminosity of an aurora is not composed haphazardly, but consists of one or more well-defined forms, such as those listed in Table VII. No doubt each represents a distinct physical process occurring in the atmosphere, though some of the forms, such as the corona, may be determined by perspective and be influenced by the position of the observer.

In the latitude of Britain an auroral display usually begins with the appearance of a *homogeneous quiet arc*

[1] Christian Wolffes. 'Gedancken über das ungewöhnliche PHOENO-MENON, welches den 17 (N.S.) Martii 1716, des Abends nach 7 Uhren zu Halle und an vielen andern Orten in und ausserhalb Deutschland gesehen worden. Wie er sie den 24 Martii in einer Lectione Publica auf der Universität zu Halle eröffnet: HALLE 1716.'

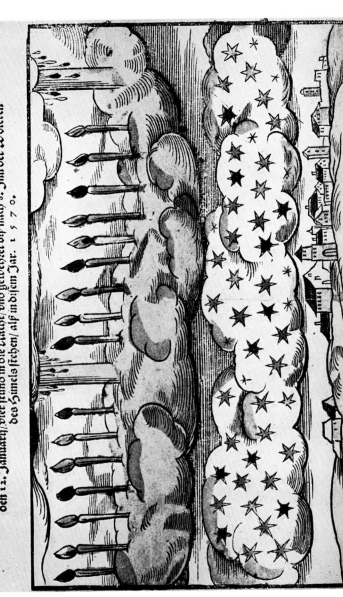

PLATE VIII.—EARLY DRAWING OF AN AURORA

'A shocking prodigy which was seen from Kuttenberg in the kingdom of Bohemia and independently in other towns and places round about on the 12th January, for four hours in the night, and lasted until after 8. As it stood within the clouds of the sky in this year 1570.' (Original print in the Crawford Library, Royal Observatory, Edinburgh, and reproduced by courtesy of the Astronomer Royal for Scotland.)

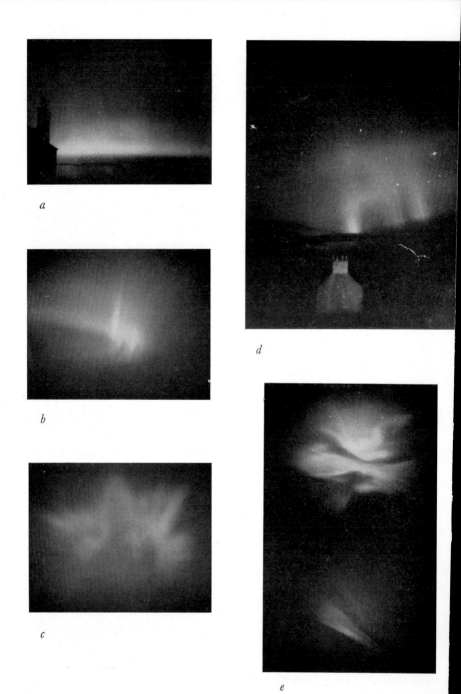

Plate IX.—AURORAL PHOTOGRAPHS

Auroral photographs taken by Mr. James Paton from Abernethy, Perthshire.
(a) Quiet arc (H. A.), 1947 September 22; (b) Drapery and rays (D. and R.),
1951 April 12; (c) Corona (C.) in magnetic zenith, 1951 October 28; (d) Part
of rayed arc (R.A.), 1949 March 17; (e) Coronae (C.), 1949 January 25.

TABLE VII

1. *Forms without ray structure*		2. *Forms with ray structure*	
Homogeneous quiet arcs	H.A.	Arcs with ray structure	R.A.
Homogeneous bands .	H.B.	Bands with ray structure	R.B.
Pulsating arcs . . .	P.A.	Draperies	D.
Diffuse luminous sur-		Rays	R.
faces	D.S.	Corona	C.
Pulsating surfaces . .	P.S.		
Feeble glow near hori-		3. *Flaming Aurorae* . . .	F.
zon	G.		

(H.A.). This is visible as a pale green arch low down in the northern sky (Plate IX); it is usually sharply bounded on its lower edge and more diffuse on top. It represents a sheet of luminosity, at a height of about 100 km. (62 miles) above the earth, and when thus seen from a distance of some hundreds of kilometres it naturally partakes of the earth's curvature. The segment of sky below the arc appears strangely dark by contrast—the black cloud so often referred to in the early accounts. The arc may remain quiescent for long periods, or it may quickly develop rays along its upper edge. These project vertically towards the zenith and may move laterally along the arc. Many of the other forms (1 and 2, Table VII) may be simultaneously visible at this stage.

Most fascinating to watch are the *pulsating arcs* (P.A.). In the great auroral display of 1951 September 25, the writer, observing from Edinburgh, studied a number of these arcs which could be seen stretching across the sky from east to west through the zenith. By locating them against the background of stars, it was clear that there were three or four parallel, conducting channels, separated from one another by perhaps half a degree. First one channel would become luminous from end to end, like a search-light beam, last for 5 seconds or so, and then fade away. The neighbouring channel would next light up for a similar period and die down. This behaviour was repeated over and over again for about a quarter of

M

an hour, each channel retaining its identity throughout the pulsations. *Pulsating surfaces* (P.S.) behave in the same mysterious way, but these are diffuse patches of irregular shape which appear and disappear rhythmically without change of position. *Diffuse luminous surfaces* (D.S.) are less active and may cover large areas of the sky for long periods. They are often brightly coloured, green or red.

During an active display the homogeneous arc with its ray structure may rise higher and higher in the northern sky, as it extends southwards, until eventually it is seen overhead. The rays then appear to converge to a single point in the sky, known as the magnetic zenith, and form there a brilliant *corona*. The magnetic zenith is the direction towards which a magnet needle would point if it were perfectly free to set itself along the lines of force of the earth's field. In these latitudes the magnetic zenith is some 20° south of the true zenith—the point vertically overhead. When the auroral rays reach this part of the sky we are observing them along their length, and they appear to converge (Plate IX*c*), just as parallel search-lights do, when seen in perspective from below.

The *flaming aurora* is a remarkable form. It appears to consist of 'waves of excitation' which move upwards from the northern horizon to the magnetic zenith, following one another in rapid succession every few seconds. As these waves pass upwards they light up rays, arcs and draperies, which in the intervals are quite invisible; one gains the vivid impression of a dying fire being fanned into flame by puffs of wind passing through it. Towards the end of the 1951 display, referred to above, these waves lasted for a whole hour and were finally followed by a corona.

Almost all colours have been seen in aurorae. That which predominates, especially in the arcs, is greenish-yellow—the colour of plants grown in the dark, as it has been most aptly described. Luminous surfaces and

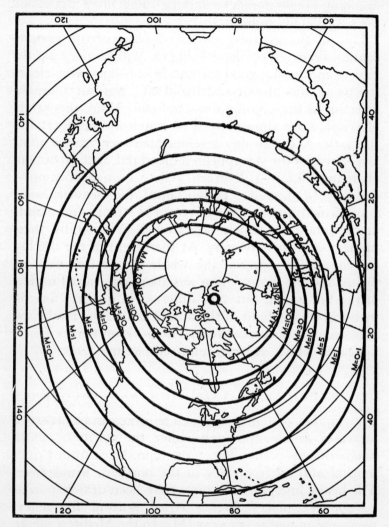

FIG. 7.1.—The geographical distribution of auroral frequency in the northern hemisphere (after Fritz). The heavy lines connect places having the same auroral frequency in nights per year (**M**). **A** is the magnetic axis point.

draperies are often red, or dark red. Pale blues and violet are occasionally noticed.

One of the greatest auroral displays of the present century occurred on the evening of 1938 January 25. By a piece of unusual good fortune British skies were clear, the moon was absent and the B.B.C. put out a timely warning in the evening news bulletin. Many thousands of people were thus enabled to watch an unforgettable spectacle. As the display developed between 7 and 8 p.m., large areas of the sky appeared blood red, with streamers changing colour—pale-green, yellow, orange, crimson— drifting, brightening, fading, until the heavens were transformed into a dome of coloured streaks and clouds of delicate tints which beggared description by their mystery and their novelty. At the height of the display the luminosity covered the whole sky as far south as Sirius, and the illumination was about equivalent to that of the full moon, but very different in quality; for the monochromatic light of the aurora makes the landscape take on an eerie appearance. The fields on that occasion appeared white, as in an infra-red picture.

GEOGRAPHICAL DISTRIBUTION AND FREQUENCY

The number of nights on which aurorae can be observed increases as we approach either the north or south magnetic axis points. Fig. 7.1 is reproduced from Fritz's map of auroral frequency in the northern hemisphere. The heavy lines, or isochasms, have been drawn in so as to connect places having equal auroral frequency, measured in nights per year (**M**). In the Mediterranean, for example, the figure **M** = o·1 indicates that only one aurora is seen, on the average, in ten years. Proceeding northwards, the frequency of visibility increases rapidly until we reach the maximum zone which encircles the magnetic axis at a distance from it of about 23°, passing just south of Iceland. Here aurorae are visible on almost every clear night. Even in the north of Scotland we find that aurorae are twenty times more frequent than in the south of England.

In the southern hemisphere the frequency of the aurora *australis* is similarly related to the distance of the observer from the southern axis point, though the available data are much less numerous and no satisfactory frequency chart has yet been produced.

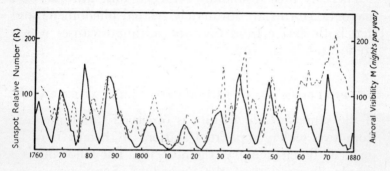

FIG. 7.2.—Relationship between auroral visibility (*dashed line*) and sunspot numbers (*full line*). The auroral observations refer to the whole of Scandinavia (after Tromholt). Note that the maximum visibility appears to lag behind the sunspot maxima. Observations were probably deficient in the earlier years.

Whatever the latitude, auroral frequency from year to year shows a close relationship to the sunspot number curve. This is illustrated in Fig. 7.2 where Tromholt has plotted for a whole century the number of auroral days per year against the sunspot number. Egedal, who studied the details of this relationship, found that auroral displays were most frequent about 1 day after the passage of large sunspots across the sun's central meridian, a similar dependence to that found by Maunder for great magnetic storms. In more recent years, Paton and McInnes have analysed the reports of aurorae made by observers in Scotland and by air-line navigators on night-time flights across the north Atlantic. They find in these records strong evidence of 27-day recurrences, coinciding in time with the minor magnetic storms of the M-region type. The writer has also noticed on several occasions a striking parallelism between the development of individual auroral displays and the simultaneous changes in the magnetic elements at near-by magnetic stations.

There is thus abundant evidence that aurorae and magnetic storms are intimately related phenomena and that both derive from the same ultimate causes which are located in the sun.

POSITION AND HEIGHT OF THE AURORA

If the same auroral feature is observed simultaneously from two widely separated stations its height may be deduced by elementary trigonometry. The following is a simple illustration of the procedure. Some years ago Prof. Lovell, of the Jodrell Bank Experimental Station near Manchester, was carrying out experiments on the reflections of short radio waves from aurorae. The writer used to warn him by telephone whenever an aurora was visible from Edinburgh. One evening, an auroral arch being seen overhead in Edinburgh, a telephone call was put through to Jodrell Bank. The answer came back: 'Many thanks. We've already seen it and are getting reflections. It's visible to us in the northern sky at an altitude of about 20°.' Since the two places lie north–south at a distance of 290 km., we obtain the approximate height, from a right-angled triangle, to be 290 tan 20°, or 105 km.

Owing to the rapid movements of most auroral features, precise measurements of height require pairs of photographs to be taken at the same instant from two

places separated by about 50 km. The Norwegian observers, Størmer, Vegard, Harang and others, have
established a network of stations for this purpose in
Scandinavia, and a similar network is now operated by
Paton and his colleagues in Scotland. The observers are
in communication by telephone, direct their cameras to
the same region of the sky and expose them simultaneously. The positions of the same auroral ray, or of some
specially luminous feature, are then compared against
the background of the stars which appear on both
photographs.

The most frequent height for the lower limits of the
quiet arcs is found to be 105 km. (65 miles), with values
ranging between 90 km. and 150 km. The vertical
depth of the luminosity in these arcs is about 15 km. But
when rays are visible they are found to extend upwards
to heights of 200–300 km. Størmer discovered that the
highest features of all are the 'sunlit' rays which extend
upwards out of the earth's shadow and pass into the
region of the atmosphere where the sun is shining; the tops
of these rays may reach 800–1,000 km. (500–600 miles).

THE SPECTRUM OF THE AURORA

During a bright aurora, a small pocket spectroscope
directed towards the sky tells us at once what is the
characteristic composition of its spectrum; the light from
every part of an aurora consists of emission lines at discrete wavelengths, and there is no evidence of any continuous spectrum. The detailed study of the emission
lines has led to many valuable discoveries: we obtain, for
example, information about the gases in the high atmosphere whose atoms and molecules are stimulated to emit
these rays; about the energies of the bombarding particles
which are required to excite them to emission; as well as
the temperature of the atmosphere at great heights.

The eye, when properly dark adapted, is an extremely sensitive instrument, and it was a long time before spectrographs and photographic plates of adequate sensitivity could be developed to record the auroral spectrum on a large scale. Vegard, in 1912, found it necessary to expose his spectral plates night after night for as long as a month in order to obtain a record of even the brightest lines. Even with modern spectrographs of high light power only the spectrum of the brightest features can be obtained with an exposure time as short as 5 minutes.

The strongest lines in the visible region of the spectrum occur at wavelengths 5,577 A.—the green line—and at 6,300, 6,363 A.—the red doublet. These three are produced by atomic oxygen—that is molecular oxygen which has been dissociated into separate atoms by the action of solar ultra-violet light. The famous green line is that which is responsible for the yellow-green colour characteristic of so many auroral features, while the doublet provides the red tints which are typical of the greatest displays and those which reach into low latitudes.

The origin of the green line remained for many years one of the unsolved problems of physics; for all attempts to produce it by the excitation of likely atmospheric gases in the laboratory had failed. Eventually it was reproduced by McLennan and Shrum (1925) in a strong electric discharge containing oxygen diluted with helium, and it was shown to arise from one of the metastable states of the oxygen atom.

In the normal course when an atom absorbs energy one of its planetary electrons is raised to a higher energy level; but it only remains in this excited state for a very short time—about 100 millionths of a second—before it unloads this surplus energy to generate a light quantum of definite frequency. The metastable states, however, have much longer life-times, reckoned in tenths of a second. To radiate from one of these states the atom must be left alone for at least such a period. Collision with another atom during the interval will remove energy and prevent the radiation process being completed. Thus it is only in gases at very low densities, where collisions are sufficiently rare, that such spectral lines can be observed. The spectra of planetary nebulae show many similar lines which were at one time attributed to a new element 'nebulium'. The long time intervals between atomic collisions in the gaseous nebulae and in the high atmosphere favour the production of these lines.

In addition to the three atomic oxygen lines, from which the main visible luminosity of the aurora is derived, there are many bands due to the nitrogen molecule. The most intense occur at wavelengths 3,914, 4,378 and 4,708 A., and it is these bands that are responsible for the various shades of blue and violet which are found in the higher auroral features. The intensity measures made by Vegard and Harang show that the green oxygen line is strongest in the low level luminosity of the arcs and rays and that the blue and violet bands of nitrogen become relatively stronger at the higher levels.

THEORIES OF THE AURORA

When we come to consider the nature of the process by which the luminescence of the aurora is generated we meet with a wide variety of opinions.

In the Chapman-Ferraro theory of magnetic storms, discussed in the last chapter, the earth is assumed to capture many of the particles from the passing solar stream, and these form a current ring in space well outside the earth's atmosphere. But some of the particles are considered to reach the earth itself and to penetrate into the upper atmosphere, especially in the polar regions. Chapman thus attributes the auroral spectrum 'to strong excitation by impact, due to particles, whether ions or electrons, entering the atmosphere from outside, with high speed'. The energy necessary to excite the lines of atomic oxygen and molecular nitrogen is derived from the kinetic energies of these bombarding particles of solar origin.

Without necessarily casting doubt upon the general conception of solar corpuscular streams, later workers have found many difficulties in accepting the view that aurorae are caused by direct particle bombardment in this way. For example, the aurora has all the appearances of being a discharge in a gas at low pressure. It is very difficult to conceive of such remarkable repetitive effects as the pulsating arcs, pulsating surfaces and flaming aurorae being caused purely by particle impact.

Again, the nitrogen bands require for their excitation an energy of 20 e.v. If the bombarding particles are electrons, as postulated by Birkeland and Størmer, and if they travel from the sun in 26 hours ($V = 1600$ km./sec.), they would possess insufficient energy; a travel time of less than 16 hours would be needed. Positively charged atoms, on account of their greater mass, might possess sufficient energy and penetrating power to reach down to levels as low as 90 km. Atoms of hydrogen would naturally be the most abundant constituent of the solar particle streams, and we might expect, therefore, to find the hydrogen line $H\alpha$ appearing in the auroral spectrum. This has been recorded only on a few occasions. During the auroral display of 1950 August 18, Meinel at Yerkes Observatory obtained a spectrum of auroral features in the magnetic zenith which showed this line. The line was displaced to the violet side of its normal position, from which it was inferred that the emitting atoms of hydrogen were streaming down the lines of force of the earth's field towards the observer at a speed of some 3,000 km./sec. Spectra from other parts of the sky showed the line undisplaced. Further experiments of this kind with fast spectrographs will be of great interest.

In Alfvén's theory of magnetic storms and aurorae, the main function of the solar particle stream is assumed to be the generation of an electric field in the environment of the earth. When this voltage between stream and ionosphere reaches a sufficient value a gaseous discharge occurs. The discharge carries heavy currents between the stream out in space and some conducting layer in the polar atmosphere, possibly the E-layer. These currents, that is rapid streams of ions and electrons, generate the magnetic storm disturbances and give rise to the luminescence of the aurora.

Hoyle, likewise, regards the aurora as being caused by a discharge, but the mechanism he proposes is somewhat different. He believes that the solar particle stream carries a magnetic field along with it to great distances from the sun. When the stream approaches the earth, neutral points are established out in space at places where the magnetic field of the stream is equal and opposite to that of the earth. Conditions at the neutral points are favourable to the acceleration of particles from the stream, after the manner of Giovanelli's theory of particle acceleration at the neutral points near sunspots, and these particles are then guided into the terrestrial ionosphere along the lines of force of the earth's field, arriving mainly in polar regions. Hoyle finds that the particles may thus acquire energies of the order of 40,000 e.v., which would be sufficient to enable electrons to penetrate down to the 100 km. level and to generate the auroral spectrum through their impacts with atmospheric atoms and molecules.

Radio echoes from the aurora were obtained in 1947

by Lovell, Clegg and Ellyett, who directed beams of short-wave pulses at the visible luminosity. These reflections have since been recorded on a number of occasions, and when their interpretation is fully understood many existing uncertainties may be resolved. In particular, precise information may be gained about heights and electron densities, and the frequency with which aurorae occur during daylight.

OTHER AURORAL EFFECTS

The aurora is becoming increasingly difficult to observe in the illuminated skies of our crowded island. This is brought home very forcibly when one has the good fortune to witness an auroral display in the jet-black skies of the north of Scotland, or in the Western Isles, several hundred miles from the reflected glare of city lights. But even if its brilliance is often dimmed by our local illuminations, there are some consequences of the aurora which manifest themselves in other ways.

The abnormal electric currents which flow in the ionosphere at such times are not confined to the conducting regions of the upper atmosphere; similar currents are induced in the earth's surface. Insulated wires extending over many miles, such as telephone and cable lines, pick up high voltages, and the resulting currents often disrupt normal communications. These earth-current disturbances are familiar to all telephone operators in high latitudes; they have even been made use of by the Norwegian watchers as a warning that aurorae are to be expected the same evening.

The interference with radio transmissions during aurorae and magnetic storms has already been mentioned. The height of the auroral arches and streamers —between 100 and 500 km. above the earth's surface— places them in the same region of the atmosphere as the

E- and F-layers upon which we rely for radio communication round the globe. It is natural that the particle streams, or electrical discharges, which give rise to the auroral luminosity will profoundly affect the state of these ionized regions. So far as the F_2-layer is concerned, the principal effect is a decrease in the electron concentration, so that reflections of the normal short-wave frequencies cease. These radio 'black-outs' in polar regions may be prolonged. At the same time the electron concentration of the E-layer appears to increase and to become irregular in distribution, but our knowledge of these changes is still very inadequate.

One curious aspect of the aurora which has received insufficient attention is the frequency of reports that audible sounds accompany the very strong displays. These have been variously described as 'cracklings', 'hissings' and 'breaking of undergrowth', and have been reported, not only in the Arctic and in Norway, but also in the south of England during the aurora of 1938. Some of these descriptions came from people who had never before seen an aurora, and who were quite unaware that such sounds had previously been heard at these times, all of which tends to show that there must be some basis of fact underlying such accounts.

Thunder is inaudible at a distance of about 10 miles, as anyone may verify for himself by timing the interval which elapses between the lightning flash and the report which follows. It is scarcely to be supposed, therefore, that any sound which might accompany the aurora would be of sufficient intensity to be audible at ten times this distance. Moreover, the atmospheric pressure 100 km. above the earth is so low that sound could not be propagated at all in these regions. It follows that the auroral noises, if genuine, must arise from some local electrification of the atmosphere near ground level, possibly giving rise to discharges from objects, such as buildings and trees, into the air surrounding them. These sounds might be heard within a limited range.

The Belgian astronomer, Montigny, noticed that stars appear to twinkle more strongly during auroral displays, and he reported similar observations made by Ussher, Forbes and others. Twinkling—or scintillation, to use the scientific term—arises from the passage across the line of sight of refractional irregularities in the atmosphere. These are situated within about 5 km. (16,000 feet) of ground level; and it is difficult to believe that auroral activity could influence the turbulence of the atmosphere at such low altitudes. However, this matter may soon be put to a quantitative test, since it is now possible, by photoelectric means, to measure both the amplitude and the frequency of these fluctuations of starlight.

In recent years the radio astronomers have demonstrated that 'radio stars' also scintillate, as is shown by the fluctuations in strength of the radio noise received from them. The cause is analogous to visual scintillation; but in this case the refractional irregularities are located in the F-layer of the ionosphere. Strong winds occur at this height, and irregular patches, or clouds of electrons, a few kilometres in dimensions, are caused to drift rapidly across the line of radio vision, bending the incoming waves to and fro. Little and Maxwell, who have made many measurements of the phenomenon, find that during aurorae and magnetic storms the rate of this scintillation shows a fourfold increase. Their method provides a further means of studying the disturbances caused in the high atmosphere by auroral activity.

DAYLIGHT AURORAE

There is good reason for supposing that aurorae occur with the same frequency in the day-time as at night. Owing, however, to the extreme faintness of the luminosity it is only the very greatest displays which have been seen against a daylight sky. One of the most circumstantial of such accounts is that given by Dr. Henry Ussher.[1] He says:

On Saturday night, May 24, 1788, there was a very bright aurora borealis (seen from Dublin), the coruscating rays of which united, as usual, in the pole of the dipping needle (magnetic zenith).[2] I have always observed that an aurora borealis renders the stars remarkably unsteady in the telescope. The next morning, about eleven, finding the stars flutter much, I examined the state of the sky, and saw whitish rays ascending from every part of the horizon, all tending to the pole of the dipping needle, where at their union they formed a small thin and white canopy, similar to the luminous one exhibited by an aurora in the night. These rays coruscated or shivered from the horizon to their point of union.

These effects were distinctly seen by three different people, and their point of union marked separately by each of them.[3]

Ussher's observation, and the few other similar accounts reported by Fritz, suggest that it would be rewarding to scrutinize the daylight sky at all times when great magnetic storms are known to be in operation. Transmission filters are now available which allow the auroral green line to pass through while greatly reducing the unwanted radiations from the sky.

[1] F.T.C.D., F.R.S. First Professor of Astronomy in the University of Dublin.
[2] This was one of the great displays of the eighteenth century (M. A. E.).
[3] *An account of an AURORA BOREALIS seen in full sunshine. Transactions of the Royal Irish Academy*, Vol. 2, p. 189.

CHAPTER VIII

Radio Waves from the Sun

DISCOVERY OF SOLAR RADIO EMISSION

SIR OLIVER LODGE—one of the great pioneers of radio—suggested in 1894 that it would be worth while to search for radio waves coming from the sun. That was a remarkable prophecy, the fulfilment of which, nearly fifty years later, forms the subject of the present chapter.

Radio waves and light waves have the same fundamental nature; they obey the same laws of physics and differ only in their wavelengths. We have seen that the intensity of the radiation emitted by a perfect radiator at any given wavelength depends uniquely upon its temperature. The diagram in Fig. 3 (Chapter I) shows us that the distribution of the sun's radiation among the various wavelengths in the visible and infra-red regions of the spectrum conforms fairly closely to that which we expect from such a radiator at 6,000° K. Short radio waves are ten million times longer than those of visible light. Nevertheless, if we treat the sun as a black body for emission in radio wavelengths, we can similarly calculate [1] what power we should receive from it in the radio spectrum at the earth's distance. (The wavelengths we are concerned with here are those ranging from 1 cm. to 20 metres; for, as we have noticed earlier, waves both shorter and longer than these will fail to penetrate the earth's atmosphere.) At a wavelength of 1 metre, for example, we would expect the incoming solar energy to

[1] See Appendix 5.

be about one thousand times less than that which could be detected with the most sensitive short-wave receiver equipped with a simple di-pole aerial system. Consequently, the prospect of being able to pick up these solar radio emissions was not a very hopeful one for the early experimenters; they were naturally banking upon the sun behaving as if it were a black body radiating at a temperature of 6,000° K.

This situation, however, was completely transformed by a number of later discoveries—discoveries so novel and so unexpected that they could not possibly have been foreseen at the time. In the first place, we now know that the radio waves which the sun emits in the metre waveband are generated not at the level of the photosphere, where the temperature is 6,000° K., but high up in the corona, in a region where the temperature is 10^{6}° K.; other things being equal the radio power received is directly proportional to the effective temperature of the source. These are the conditions which exist when there are no sunspots or flares on the disk—the quiet 'radio-sun', as it is now called.

Secondly, when the sun is active—that is when large sunspots or flares are present—the radio noise may be a million times in excess of that which is received from the quiet sun. When one of these 'noisy' sunspots is near the centre of the disk the radio power emitted is equal to that which we would expect to receive from the whole sun if it were at a temperature of 10^{10}° K.; and the presence of an intense flare may raise this apparent temperature to 10^{13}° K. Thus the strength of the radio emission on these occasions is far in excess of anything the early experimenters had contemplated.

Now, let us return to the correct order of events. In 1931, Jansky made the remarkable discovery that radio waves were reaching the earth from outer space. Working at a frequency of 20 Mc./s. (15 metres wavelength) and letting the sky drift across his aerial beam, he showed that these waves varied diurnally both in strength and in the direction of their arrival. When he timed the repetitions of maximum intensity he found that they were not precisely 24 hours apart; the interval was $23^h 56^m$, which is the period of rotation of the earth relative to the stars. Later, he showed that the strongest emission came from the belt of the Milky Way, where he found an intensity maximum towards the galactic centre in Sagittarius. These results were confirmed by Reber, who found secondary maxima in Cygnus and Cassiopeia; the source of the waves must, therefore, be either the stars themselves, or the interstellar matter lying in the plane of the galaxy.

The discovery of cosmic radio waves and its subsequent exploitation by means of radio telescopes has already opened up a new view of the universe. On visible wavelengths, dust and gas clouds blot out nine-tenths of the galaxy from our vision: the much longer radio waves penetrate this fog and enable us to see right through our Milky Way star system to its furthest boundary.

After this success it was natural that radio aerials should be turned towards the nearest of the stars—the sun—to ascertain if it also was a radio source. But it was not until 1943 that Southworth was able to record solar radio emissions on centimetre wavelengths. The intensities were such as led him to conclude that the sun had an effective temperature of 18,000° K. In the following year Reber also made successful observations, this time at metre wavelengths.

AERIALS OF HIGH GAIN

Both these workers had greatly enhanced the sensitivity of their receivers by using aerials of high power gain. Such aerials consist of groups of di-poles suitably spaced, or a paraboloid system (Fig. 8.1) such as that which is

now used in many large radio telescopes. The paraboloid collects the radio waves which are directed towards it along its axis and concentrates them upon a
receiving aerial placed at the focus (F) in the same
manner as the silvered mirror of an astronomical telescope
collects the light waves which reach it and directs them
into the eye, or into the latent image of a photographic
plate. The power gain (G) of such an aerial is given by

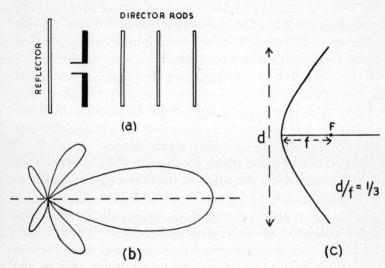

FIG. 8.1.—Aerials of high power gain for solar radio noise reception:
(a) Yagi aerial system, (b) polar diagram of Yagi aerial beam,
(c) paraboloid aerial.

$G = 4\pi A/\lambda^2$, that is to say it is directly proportional to
the area (A) of the aperture and inversely proportional
to the square of the wavelength (λ). Unlike systems of
di-poles, these paraboloidal aerials can operate on a
range of wavelengths, although it is clear that the power
gain is greatest for the shorter waves. The largest mirror
aerial of this kind now in use is that at Jodrell Bank; it is
220 feet in diameter and produces a gain of 1,200 times
on a wavelength of 4 metres.

WARTIME DISCOVERIES

During the war radar transmitting and receiving installations (4 to 6 metre band) for spotting aircraft were widely distributed throughout Britain. On 1942 February 27 and 28, many sets recorded strong sources of noise which were at first thought to be due to enemy interference. But several observers, who were able to follow the noise in bearing and in elevation, found that in every case their aerials were directed towards the sun. At this time a great sunspot, whose maximum area exceeded 2,000 millionths of the hemisphere, was near the centre of the solar disk. Its central meridian passage occurred on the 28th. From noon onwards on that day there was visible over the sunspot one of the most brilliant flares the writer has ever seen. It exceeded the area of the sunspot itself and lasted for over three hours.

When Appleton and Hey reported these phenomena in 1945, they drew attention to the many earlier accounts of 'hissing' noises which had been heard during the solar maximum years of 1936–38 by amateurs using shortwave receivers at 10 metres wavelength. These noises had only been audible when large sunspots were present and they had never been heard at night. Since the amateur receivers had aerials of low power gain, it was evident that the intrinsic power of these solar radio emissions must have been very great indeed, and far in excess of the expected black body noise values. These facts were confirmed by Appleton and Hey on the occasion of the next big sunspot which became visible (Plate I) in February 1946. Many flares occurred while this spot was crossing the disk, and these workers were able to show that the greatest bursts of radio noise occurred at the times of the flares.

NEED FOR HIGHER RESOLVING POWER

The immensely greater penetrating power of radio waves, due to their freedom from scattering by dust and atoms in space, has to be paid for at a price. That price is the low resolving power of radio telescopes; the greater the wavelength employed the less the resolving power. For instance, a visual telescope with a mirror, or lens, 5 inches in diameter will discriminate between two stars which have an angular separation of 1 second of arc. To equal this performance a radio telescope would require a mirror aerial 1,000 miles in diameter!

High resolving power is of the utmost importance in the study of solar radio noise; first of all, we wish to be able to pick out the small areas—spots, flares, etc.—which are the source points of the strongest noise, and secondly to measure the distribution of the weaker background noise coming from the undisturbed solar surface without interference from these much stronger local transmitters.

Many different devices have been used to increase the resolving power. All are related to well-known interference experiments in optics, where they have previously been used either to increase the resolving power of optical instruments or for exact measurements of the wavelength of light. The first application of these principles to radio was the *sea interferometer* (Fig. 8.2*a*), constructed by McCready, Pawsey and Payne-Scott in 1946, and employed by them to pinpoint the radio waves coming from the great sunspot (Plate I) of February in that year. An aerial, mounted upon a cliff 250 feet above the level of the sea, was set to face the rising sun, the radio waves being received directly from the sunspot and by reflection from the surface of the sea below. Interference occurred between the direct and reflected rays. As the sun rose higher in the sky the waves, arriving by the two different routes, stepped in and out of phase with the varying path difference (OQ–OP, Fig. 8.2). The sharp maxima and minima of the signals provided proof, not merely that the noise emanated from the sun's disk, but that it was localized in a small strip of

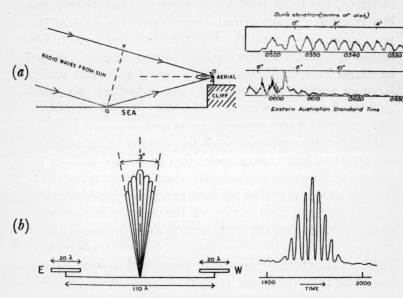

FIG. 8.2.—Radio interferometers for high resolving power: (*a*) sea interferometer, and interference pattern produced by radio noise from an active sunspot as sun rises over horizon; reproduced (redrawn) from the *Proceedings of the Royal Society*, A, **190,** 366, 1947, by courtesy of the editors and Drs. L. L. McCready, J. L. Pawsey and R. Payne-Scott ; (*b*) spaced aerial interferometer, as used by Ryle and Smith, showing fan-shaped radiation pattern and noise record as point source transits across the beam; reproduced (redrawn) from *Reports on Progress in Physics*, **13,** 184, 1950, by courtesy of the editors and Mr. M. Ryle.

the disk which also contained the large sunspot. The apparent diameter of the solar disk is 32 minutes of arc, and this arrangement gave a resolving power of about 8 minutes of arc. The method is analogous to the 'Lloyd's mirror' experiment in optics.

A radio interferometer of another kind was developed in the same year by Ryle and Vonberg at Cambridge. In its final form this consisted of two systems of di-pole aerials each 20 wavelengths long (Fig. 8.2*b*), the centres of which were spaced 110 wavelengths apart upon an E–W line. The reception pattern of such an aerial system covers a narrow band of sky about 3° wide, running N–S along the meridian, and with a suitable tilt of the aerials the band can be made to extend from the celestial equator to the north pole. The interference between the aerials further divides this 3° band into narrower channels about $\frac{1}{2}$° apart. In effect, the arrangement shuts out all radio waves from the sky except those which enter through these half-dozen or so parallel 'slits' extending along the meridian. With the rotation of the earth the parallel slits sweep slowly across the stellar background. When the slits scan an extended radio source, like the Milky Way, a steady, or slowly varying, signal is recorded, but a sharply defined source, subtending an angle of $\frac{1}{2}$° or less, produces a series of well-defined maxima and minima in the signal. From the shapes and times of these variations both the size of the source and its position in the sky can be obtained with surprising accuracy. The device is similar in principle to the Michelson optical interferometer which was used twenty years ago to increase the resolving power of the 100-inch telescope.

Lastly, the principle of the optical diffraction grating has been applied to radio by Christiansen and Warburton (1953). In their arrangement, 32 parabolic aerials, each $5\frac{1}{2}$ feet in diameter, are strung out at intervals of 23 feet along an E–W line. The parabolas are linked together so that all can be directed to the same point in the sky. Working at a wavelength of 21 centimetres, this remarkable instrument enables its constructors to discriminate between sources of radio waves on the sun which are separated by an angle of only 2 minutes of arc (equivalent to one-sixteenth of the sun's disk).

RADIO NOISE FROM THE QUIET SUN

By the use of such aerial devices, giving high angular resolution, it is possible to discriminate between the noise contributions of (*a*) the sun itself—the 'quiet' sun,

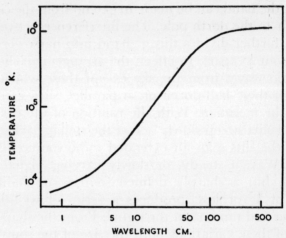

FIG. 8.3.—Apparent temperatures of the quiet sun deduced from the observed intensities of radio noise on different wavelengths.

as it is called, (*b*) local active regions on the sun's disk, and (*c*) the galactic background in the same part of the sky. Measures of the intensity of the quiet solar noise have thus been made for a number of wavelengths between 1 cm. and 10 metres. These intensities are usually expressed by calculating what the effective temperature of the sun must be—assuming that it radiates like a black body—in order to generate the radio power which is actually recorded on any given wavelength. The curve in Fig. 8.3 shows the results for the measures which are available.

Now, the most remarkable feature of this graph is the variation of the apparent solar temperature with wavelength. We see that the centimetre waves are generated as if the solar temperature was 10,000° K., whereas the metre waves have such intensity that they indicate a temperature greater than 1,000,000° K. This suggested to Martyn, who proposed the first satisfactory theory of the quiet solar noise, that the short and long waves must originate in different layers of the solar atmosphere; the centimetre waves coming from the cool, low-lying photosphere and the metre waves from the hot, elevated corona. Martyn went further than this: he calculated the precise heights in the atmosphere at, or above, which radio waves of given wavelength must be generated in order to succeed in escaping from the electron gas. Let us consider how this was done. As we saw earlier on, the atoms of the corona are highly ionized, and the free electron population is consequently very great. Indeed, the corona depends for its visibility upon the radiant glow of the sunlight which is scattered from these fast moving, free electrons. Baumbach, Allen, and later van de Hulst, showed how to estimate, from the measured intensities of this white scattered light, just what the number of electrons must be at different levels above the photosphere. As examples of their figures, we find that at a height of 500 km. above the photosphere there are about one hundred million free electrons present in every cubic centimetre. This number decreases steadily as we pass outwards, until at a distance of 700,000 km. (430,000 miles) above the sun's surface (that is 2·0 solar radii from the sun's centre) the electron population has fallen to one hundredth part—about one million electrons in each cubic centimetre.

Now, one million electrons per cubic centimetre is just about the electron population in the F-layer of the terrestrial ionosphere. We have also seen that radio waves are unable to escape from the earth's surface unless their frequency exceeds the critical frequency of the *F*-layer, say 7 Mc./s. (43 metres wavelength). Similarly, in the solar atmosphere at each level there is an appropriate critical frequency of escape.[1] The escape frequency becomes higher and higher as we penetrate deeper and deeper towards the photospheric level—just the opposite

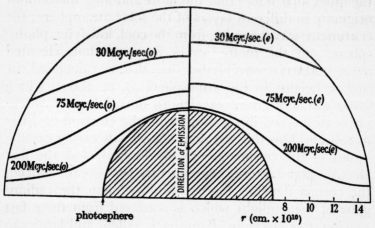

FIG. 8.4.—The levels in the corona above which radio waves of different frequencies can escape, according to Martyn's theory. The levels are given for waves circularly polarized in opposite directions by the action of the sun's magnetic field, (*o*) ordinary, (*e*) extraordinary. Reproduced from the *Proceedings of the Royal Society*, A, **193,** 44, 1948, by courtesy of the editors and Dr. D. F. Martyn.

to what happens in the *D*, *E* and *F* regions of the ionosphere. This means that waves of frequency 30,000 Mc./s. (1 cm. wavelength) generated at the photosphere, or at any level above this, can escape into space, whereas frequencies of 30 Mc./s. (10 metres wavelength) will be unable to get out, and will be absorbed, unless they are generated at heights greater than 500,000 km. Broadly speaking, therefore, the metre waves come to us from the

[1] See Appendix 6.

million degree corona; the centimetre waves from the ten-thousand degree level just above the visible surface.

These results of Martyn's calculations are shown in Fig. 8.4, where the heights above the photosphere are drawn in above which the different frequencies can escape. For each frequency two slightly different levels are shown, corresponding to radio waves which are circularly polarized in opposite directions due to the action of the sun's magnetic field. However, the field of 50 gauss, which was assumed for purposes of calculation, in 1946, is now known to be much in excess of the true value which is nearer 1 gauss. Polarization, in fact, is found to be of importance only in the case of the enhanced radiation generated in the vicinity of sunspots, where, of course, very strong fields exist. On the whole there is fairly good agreement between observation and theory for the quiet sun; it is interesting to notice that the quiet radio-sun has an observed diameter three times greater at metre wavelengths than at centimetre wavelengths.

RADIO NOISE FROM THE ACTIVE SUN

Radiations from the active, or disturbed, sun may be divided into three characteristic types:

(a) 'enhanced radiation' lasting for several days, and associated with the passage of large sunspots across the disk,

(b) 'bursts' having a duration of only a few seconds, and

(c) 'outbursts' of great intensity, lasting for 10 minutes or so, and associated with flares simultaneously observed in the spectrohelioscope.

The enhanced radiation from sunspots at metre wavelengths escapes from the sun predominantly in an upward direction. This 'beaming' effect can be seen from

Fig. 8.5*a*, taken from a paper by Hey, Parsons and Phillips, from which it is clear that the noise reaches its greatest intensity at the time of central meridian passage of the sunspot; a day or so on either side of this date the

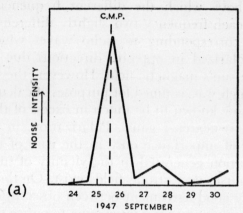

(a)

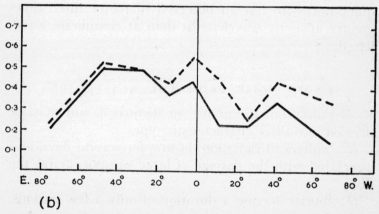

(b)

Fig. 8.5.—(*a*) Radio waves escape from an active sunspot mainly in a vertical direction, as shown by the steep rise in intensity of the noise when the spot is near the central meridian. (*b*) Noise outbursts from flares show little dependence upon solar longitude. *Full line:* No. of outbursts/No. of flares. *Broken line:* Outburst intensities/No. of flares. Both diagrams reproduced from *Monthly Notices of the Royal Astronomical Society*, **108,** 354, 1948, by courtesy of the editors and Dr. J. S. Hey, Mr. S. J. Parsons and Mr. J. W. Phillips.

intensity has a much lower value. These authors suggest that the angular beam-width is in the region of 40°. At shorter wavelengths (21 cm.) Christiansen finds that the sunspot radiation is not beamed in this way. Nor has such an effect been found in connection with the outbursts from flares; these are recorded apparently with equal intensity whether the flare is located at the centre of the disk or near the limb (see Fig. 8.5b). The radiation from sunspots is also circularly polarized, especially for the longer waves, suggesting the influence of the sunspot magnetic fields. The area from which the radiation is emitted is found to be comparable in size to the sunspot itself, and it seems probable that the source is the intensely heated corona immediately above.

The bursts are superimposed upon the enhanced radiation from sunspots. The duration of a burst is a matter of seconds, but it is found to increase with increasing wavelengths.

We have as yet no generally accepted theory as to the mechanism by which the sunspot radio emission is generated. In Ryle's view we have to envisage actual electron temperatures of the order of $10^{10°}$ K. in the corona immediately above a sunspot. He supposes that electrons acquire the velocities appropriate to these enormous temperatures by acceleration in the local electric fields which exist near the spots.

An alternative explanation in terms of 'plasma oscillations', put forward by Martyn and others, does away with the need for such high effective temperatures. A plasma is simply an electron gas, of which the corona is a good example. It was shown many years ago by J. J. Thomson that such a gas possesses a natural period of oscillation given by $T = \sqrt{\pi m / N e^2}$, where m and e are respectively the mass and charge of an electron and N is the number of free electrons per cubic centimetre. If the coronal electrons could be set in vibration near a sunspot they would generate electromagnetic waves and these might escape into space if the local conditions were favourable. The great difficulty, however, with this type of mechanism is to understand how such a vibration, once started, can be maintained. An ordinary wireless transmitter continues to radiate only for so long as energy is supplied to a tuned circuit in order to maintain its oscillations. The natural vibrations of a plasma would die out unless maintained in some such way.

Outbursts are by far the most spectacular of the solar radio emissions. In 1946 Appleton and Hey noted the coincidence in time between large enhancements of solar noise and visually observed flares. A few months later the first exact comparison was made between the development curve of a flare and the outburst of noise accompanying it (see Fig. 8.6). This flare, of 1946 July 25, was one of quite exceptional area and brilliance (see Plate III), and the associated outburst, as recorded by Lovell and Banwell, who were able to register its peak intensity, reached a level one thousand times that of the enhanced noise from the great sunspot itself.

When a number of these comparisons had been made, Hey, Parsons and Phillips noticed that there was a delay, often amounting to several minutes, between the flare 'flash' and the time of onset of the radio outburst, as measured on 73 Mc./s. (4·1 metres wavelength). There was nothing particularly remarkable in this, for it might have been supposed that the flare must reach a certain threshold of brilliance before it could generate radio waves. But Payne-Scott, Yabsley and Bolton recorded the outbursts, using simultaneously three different radio receivers, tuned to 200, 100 and 60 Mc./s. respectively. They confirmed Hey's delay times, and in addition made the most intriguing discovery that the interval between flare and outburst was always greater on the lower

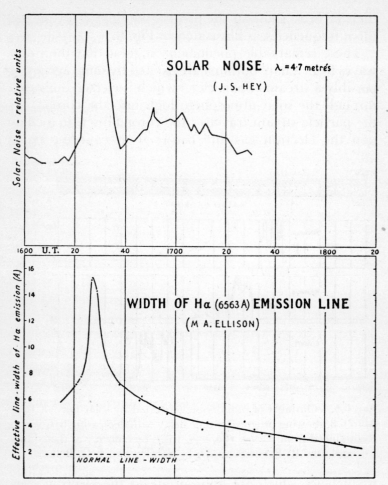

FIG. 8.6.—Radio noise outburst on wavelength of 4·7 metres (Hey) and line-width development curve during the great flare of 1946 July 25 (Ellison). Reproduced from *Nature*, **163,** 749, 1949, by courtesy of the editors.

frequencies. Thus it appeared that the effect of the flare disturbance was first to generate the short waves of high frequency, and these were then followed by the longer waves with progressively increasing delay times. One of their records, showing the progressive time delay on the three frequencies, is illustrated in Fig. 8.7.

These remarkable phenomena suggest that the radio waves from a flare outburst are excited by some agency—possibly a stream of particles—which is ejected outwards through the solar atmosphere high into the corona. As the particle stream traverses the corona it sets in oscillation the electron gas and causes it to emit the radio

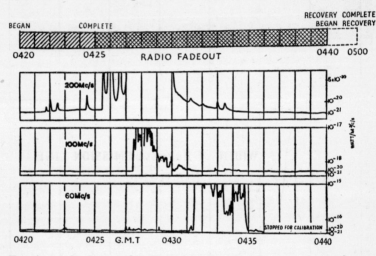

FIG. 8.7.—Outburst of radio noise generated by solar flare of 1947 March 8, showing progressive time delay with decreasing frequency. Reproduced from *Nature*, **160**, 256, 1947, by courtesy of the editors and Drs. R. Payne-Scott, D. E. Yabsley and J. G. Bolton.

frequencies which are appropriate to the electron concentrations in the successive levels (see Fig. 8.8). From Martyn's work the heights at which different frequencies originate is known. Wild has thus been able to calculate the outward velocities of the hypothetical particle streams which are believed to give rise to the outbursts. He finds speeds of the order of 500 km./sec., which is of the same order of magnitude as those acquired by the jets of luminous prominence material which we can often see being blown out from the flare regions (see Plate VII).

Further confirmation of this mechanism was obtained by Payne-Scott and Little, who were able, by means of a highly directional interferometer aerial, to locate and follow the outward motion of the source point of the outburst noise. At first the source was located near the visible flare which was situated towards the limb of the sun, and

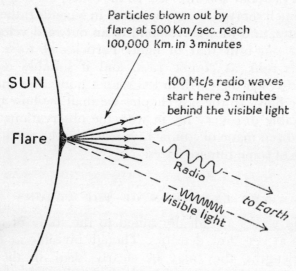

FIG. 8.8.—Radio waves generated in the corona by particles blown out from a flare.

it subsequently moved upwards during the next 30 minutes, until it reached a final height of 1·6 solar radii.

At the present time there appears to be no reason to doubt the simple hypothesis that these intense radio emissions are excited in the corona by the outward passage of particles which are expelled by the flare; and great new vistas of solar research are opened up by this technique.

Wild and his colleagues in Australia have constructed

a panoramic spectrum recorder for the study of outbursts. This is essentially a radio set which scans rapidly backwards and forwards over a given range of frequencies (40–240 Mc./s.) and automatically registers the noise intensity at each frequency against time. Wild finds that there are two characteristic types of outburst. In the first type the frequency drift is that which is to be expected for a source moving outwards through the corona at a speed of about 500 km./sec. In the other, the delay times are much shorter, being measured in seconds rather than minutes, and they correspond to an outward velocity of about one-fifth that of light. Particles of these great speeds rank as cosmic rays, and if suitably directed would reach the earth in less than 1 hour after the flash of the flare. In the last chapter we shall see how this remarkable discovery fits in with the observations which have been made of cosmic rays reaching the earth at the times of some intense flares.

THE EXTENSION OF THE CORONA

Radio waves are ideally suited to the study of ionized gases at very low densities. Though invisible at optical wavelengths, they may be clearly 'seen' in the radio wave-band. It is by such methods that our knowledge of the ionized regions of the earth's atmosphere has been built up, and such information could not have been derived in any other way.

The corona is a ball of ionized gas surrounding the sun, in which the population of free electrons falls off as we pass outwards. What are the limits of its extension into outer space? Ryle and his collaborators at Cambridge have recently carried out some very beautiful experiments in an endeavour to answer this question. It is not possible, as yet, to project radio waves towards the corona and to observe their reflections, as has been done by the pulse technique in sounding the ionosphere. But Ryle has employed the incoming radio waves from a radio star to perform a somewhat similar experiment. Each summer in June the intense radio source in Taurus is occulted by the corona, as the sun slowly traverses that particular region of the sky in its annual path along the ecliptic. It was expected that when the radio star began its passage behind the corona the waves would be refracted away from the line of sight by the coronal electrons, so that a partial eclipse of the radio star would occur. The deeper the penetration of the waves through the corona the feebler would be the signal reaching the earth.

These predictions were fully confirmed when the experiment was successfully carried out in 1952 at radio wavelengths of 3·7 metres and 7·9 metres. But the surprising feature was the fact that the waves from the radio star began to diminish in strength long before the radio star had reached the visible confines of the corona. The fading of the signals began at a distance of 10 solar diameters (9 million miles) on one side and recovery was complete at a similar distance on the other side of the sun. These results suggest that, in all probability, there is no sharp outer boundary to the coronal atmosphere, and that the coronal material may have an appreciable density out to the orbit of the earth and beyond.

CHAPTER IX

Cosmic Rays

THE PRIMARY RADIATION

ASTRONOMERS are becoming concerned more and more with the properties of the matter which lies between the stars. Interstellar clouds of dust and gas compose perhaps one-half of the total mass of the galaxy. A small fraction only of this material is visible to us—in those regions where by chance hot stars illuminate it, or where it reddens, or even extinguishes, the light of the stars beyond. We have also become aware of another part of the interstellar material—the primary cosmic rays—by reason of the enormous energies with which these particles are endowed.

The primary cosmic rays consist of positively charged atoms traversing space at speeds which approach the velocity of light. They appear to encounter the earth with a uniform distribution from all directions, and their energies lie within the range of 10^8 to 10^{17} electron-volts.[1] As we might expect, the majority of these particles are protons—the nuclei of hydrogen atoms—hydrogen being the most abundant element in the universe, but among them there is also a small proportion of heavier atoms, up to atomic weight 56—that of iron.

When these high-energy projectiles arrive in the upper levels of the atmosphere they begin to perform a remarkable series of atom splitting experiments, giving rise to

[1] An electron-volt is the energy gained by an electron falling through a potential difference of 1 volt.

nuclear explosions and to secondary particles of many types, the effects of which can be traced downwards to ground level and even far below the surface of the earth. Herein lies the great importance of cosmic ray research to the physicist; for the cosmic rays provide a natural source of bombarding particles, the energies of which have not yet been surpassed by artificial means. To the astrophysicist cosmic rays present a challenge; where do they originate and how are they propagated through space?

THE SECONDARY RADIATION

The permanent and stable bricks out of which atoms are built consist of protons, electrons and neutrons. During the violent disturbance which occurs when an atomic nucleus in the atmosphere is struck by a primary cosmic ray, or one of its products, other temporary

TABLE VIII

Properties of the Elementary Particles

Name	Mass in terms of the electron	Average lifetime before decay	Products of decay
Electron	1	Stable	—
Positron	1	Stable	—
Proton	1845	Stable	—
Neutron	1847	19 min.	Electron and proton
π meson (+)	270	10^{-8} sec.	μ meson and neutrino
π meson (−)	270	10^{-8} sec.	μ meson and neutrino
π meson (neutral)	270	10^{-13} sec.	Two photons
μ meson (+)	210	10^{-6} sec.	Electron and two neutrinos
μ meson (−)	210	10^{-6} sec.	Electron and two neutrinos
τ meson	970	$> 10^{-9}$ sec.	Three π mesons
χ meson	1000	$> 10^{-9}$ sec.	π or μ meson
V particles	(Properties still uncertain)		
Photon	0	Stable	—
Neutrino	0	Stable	—

particles come into being (Fig. 9.1). The most important group are the mesons (Table VIII), particles having masses intermediate between those of the electron and proton. At least seven different varieties of mesons have

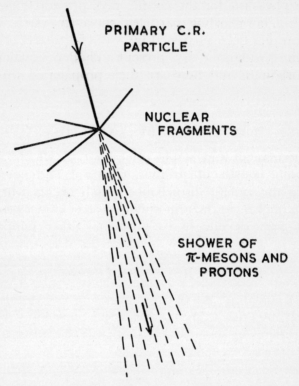

PRIMARY C.R.
PARTICLE

NUCLEAR
FRAGMENTS

SHOWER OF
π-MESONS AND
PROTONS

FIG. 9.1.—Primary cosmic ray particle disintegrates an atomic nucleus in the upper atmosphere, forming a shower of high-speed π-mesons and protons.

been identified, some charged positively, some negatively and one that is neutral. All such particles have a lifetime of one-millionth of a second or less, after which they decay spontaneously, giving rise to high-energy electrons, either positive or negative, to neutrinos, or to photons (γ-rays). These in turn produce many complex secondary reactions during their descent through the atmosphere, until finally all the original energy is degraded into heat.

The neutral π mesons are of special interest because they lead to the formation of electron showers. Owing to the excessively short lifetime of the π meson (less than one million millionth of a second) it cannot move far from its point of birth in the high atmosphere, but disintegrates spontaneously into two photons—or γ-rays—of very high energy. Each of these photons, when it enters the disturbing field of an atom, gives birth to a pair of electrons, one positive and one negative. Each electron, in turn, entering the domain of another atom, causes it to emit a photon; the photon gives rise to a further electron pair, and so on. In this way the decay of the original neutral meson develops into a shower of electrons moving downwards. The number of electrons in the shower continues to multiply until eventually the energy of the pair-producing photons falls below the value—about one million electron-volts—needed to produce these materializations of electrons. The electron showers constitute about one-quarter of the cosmic ray activity observed at ground level and their contribution at first increases with height, and then decreases in the higher levels.

Thus the cosmic ray effects which are observed near the bottom of the atmosphere arise entirely from secondary particles—the mesons and their various disintegration products.

METHODS OF RECORDING

The charged particles of cosmic ray origin are detected and recorded through the ionization they produce. Three pieces of apparatus have been principally used in these investigations. In the Geiger-Müller counter the

THE SUN AND ITS INFLUENCE

passage of a sufficiently energetic charged particle generates a shower of ions and electrons in a tube containing a suitable gas mixture. The ions and electrons cause a discharge of current from the walls of the tube to a central electrode when a high potential difference is maintained between them. Two such counters may be linked together by an electrical circuit which is designed to record only the passage of the same particle through both tubes in succession. A particle which traverses one tube and not the other will fail to be counted. This kind of arrangement is known as a cosmic ray 'telescope', since it yields valuable information about the direction of arrival of the particles.

Another device of great power is the cloud chamber, invented by Prof. C. T. R. Wilson. This contains a mixture of gas and super-saturated water vapour. A charged particle traversing the gas leaves behind it a trail of ionized atoms and electrons which serve as centres of condensation; the track of the particle is clearly marked by the water droplets which form by condensation along its path. If the cloud chamber is operated in a powerful magnetic field the curvatures of the tracks —clockwise or anti-clockwise—enable one to distinguish between particles of opposite sign, and the degree of curvature also provides a measure of the particle energy. A simple variation of this method is that in which the particles traverse not a vapour but the sensitive emulsion of a photographic plate. In these specially thick emulsions each grain of silver bromide which is struck by a charged particle is turned to silver when the plate is developed. If a primary cosmic ray, for example, happens to disintegrate the nucleus of an atom within the emulsion a complete record is obtained of the trajectories of the many dozens of particles which radiate from the encounter (Fig. 9.1). The plates have the advantage that they will store up their records over long periods, and they may be easily exposed on the tops of mountains or be raised by balloons to heights of 40 km. (25 miles) above the earth.

DISTRIBUTION IN LATITUDE AND AZIMUTH

The primary particles, shooting in from outer space, come under the influence of the earth's magnetic field, long before they reach the atmospheric barrier, and their trajectories are altered. The deflection of a charged particle traversing a magnetic field is greatest when its line of flight is at right angles to the lines of magnetic force. Positively charged protons, for example, approaching the earth in the plane of the magnetic equator will be thrown back into space unless their energy exceeds some 10^{10} e.v. And as we move away from the magnetic equator towards the magnetic poles particles of smaller and smaller energies succeed in entering the atmosphere. Now, the intensity of cosmic radiation at sea-level was found by Clay to be 10 per cent less at the magnetic equator than in high latitudes, and at higher elevations in the atmosphere the variation is larger still. This is taken to mean that the majority of the primary particles are electrically charged. If they were uncharged, like neutrons, or were composed of wave radiations, that is photons, they would experience no bending away from these regions.

Measurements made of the direction of arrival of cosmic rays also show that near the equator there is a preponderance of particles approaching from a westerly direction. This effect of azimuth indicates that a large proportion of the primaries carry *positive* charges.

The nature of the primaries can be ascertained only by sending up balloons to great altitudes where their ionization tracks may be recorded in photographic emulsions. The evidence from these explorations is that atoms of hydrogen and helium outnumber the heavier particles by about 1,000 to 1. Nevertheless, the particles of high atomic weight, although less numerous, are more efficient in supplying mesons by disintegration, for their nuclei contain many more protons than those of the lighter atoms. The number of primary particles reaching the atmosphere is about 2 per square centimetre per second at the poles and about one-tenth of this at the equator.

VARIATIONS IN TIME

Continuous measurements of the secondary cosmic radiation in the lower atmosphere have sought to establish variations which might indicate a directional effect in the travel of the primary particles through space. For example, if any appreciable number of the primaries originated in the sun, or in particular regions of the Milky Way, one might expect to find regular fluctuations related respectively to solar and sidereal time. Before conclusions can be drawn it is necessary to eliminate the small variations due to changes in atmospheric pressure and temperature, and changes in the earth's magnetic field. When this is done small residual variations of a periodic nature remain. One of these is a reduction of several per cent, recurring at intervals of 27 days over a period of months; and the other is a regular daily variation of the order of 1 per cent. Both are thought to have their origin in the sun, but the connection is at present obscure.

Variations dependent upon the position of the galaxy must be much smaller, and have not yet been detected with any certainty. This problem has become further complicated in recent years by the realization that extensive magnetic fields probably exist in the ionized gas clouds of the galaxy. Wherever in space the primaries originate, the action of these galactic magnetic fields

TABLE IX

No.	Date	Flare class	Solar longitude	Time of max. intensity U.T.	Line-width in angstroms	Cosmic ray increase at Cheltenham, Md., per cent above normal	Time lag: cosmic ray max. minus flare max.
1	1942 Feb. 28	3+	E 4°	1200*	4·1 (1242)	7	1^{h}
2	1942 Mar. 7	—	W 90 ?	0442*	—	9	1^{h}
3	1946 July 25	3+	E 15	1627	15·9 (max.)	20	2·5^{h}
4	1949 Nov. 19	3+	W 70	1032	22·9 (max.)	{43, 180 (Climax)	0·5^{h}

* Timed from radio fadeout and magnetic crochet.

will be to bend the trajectories of the charged particles to such an extent that a uniform distribution is soon established.

While the interpretation of the regular variations due to the sun is still uncertain, large fluctuations of an irregular nature and of solar origin are now clearly established. These are of two kinds: first, sudden increases which have occurred at the times of intense solar flares, and secondly, decreases during the period of great magnetic storms.

INCREASES ASSOCIATED WITH GREAT FLARES

Continuous measurements of cosmic radiation have been confined to a single cycle of solar activity. During this period four sudden increases have been recorded, and these have all coincided in time with the occurrence of intense flares on the solar disk. Needless to say, both types of phenomena are of such rarity that the odds against four chance coincidences are prohibitive.

The facts relating to these cases are summarized in Table IX. The flares 1, 3 and 4 were observed by the writer and others, and the records, both photographic and visual, indicate that they were among the greatest ever recorded. The first two were associated with the large sunspot (of area 2,000 millionths) which passed across the sun's central meridian on 1942 February 28 and reached the west limb on March 7. It may be recalled that it was this spot group and the flare of February 28 which led to the discovery of solar radio noise by Hey. No. 3 occurred over the fourth largest recorded sunspot (No. 4 of Table II, page 40) when it was near the centre of the disk. This flare is illustrated in Plate III and its development curve is shown in Fig. 8.6. No. 4 was located over a smaller, highly active, developing sunspot as it was nearing the west limb. No. 2 passed unobserved any-

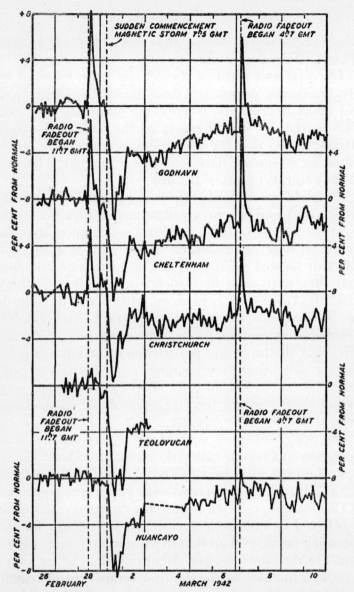

FIG. 9.2.—Sudden increases of cosmic radiation at the times of two intense flares, 1942 February 28 and March 7. Also decrease at time of great magnetic storm, February 29. Reproduced from *Physical Review*, **79**, 501, 1950, by courtesy of the editors and Drs. S. E. Forbush, T. B. Stinchcomb and M. Schein.

where in the world, but we may conclude from its iono-spheric effects that it also was of 3+ importance.

The first and third of these flares were followed by great magnetic storms with delay times of $19\frac{1}{2}$ hours and $26\frac{1}{2}$ hours respectively, whereas the other two were not. This is what we should expect on the basis of Newton's statistical law, that the probability of a magnetic storm following an intense flare is greater if the flare is located in the central regions of the disk.

The sudden cosmic ray effects, as reported by Forbush, Stinchcomb and Schein, are illustrated in Figs. 9.2, 3 and 4. From a study of these diagrams it transpires that the increases were not recorded at the station Huancayo which is located on the earth's magnetic equator, and that they were most in evidence at middle and high magnetic latitudes (Cheltenham, Md., magnetic latitude 50° N; Godhavn, Greenland, magnetic latitude 80° N). From this circumstance two conclusions can be drawn: first, that the incoming particles were mainly charged, and secondly, that their energies could not have greatly exceeded 10^{10} electron-volts. Particles endowed with higher energy would have penetrated the earth's field even at the magnetic equator.

On 1949 November 19 a cosmic ray recorder was in operation at Climax, Colorado, at an altitude of 11,500 feet. Here the increase was 180 per cent of the normal value (Fig. 9.4), as compared with 43 per cent registered at Cheltenham, near sea-level. This variation with height is believed to indicate a somewhat lower energy for the incoming particles than that of the normal cosmic radiation. On the same occasion Adams at Manchester found a six-fold increase in the neutron component of cosmic rays, followed by a slow decline which persisted until long after sunset on the same day. Adams and Braddick consider that these facts are also consistent with the arrival of charged primary particles from the sun, having energies

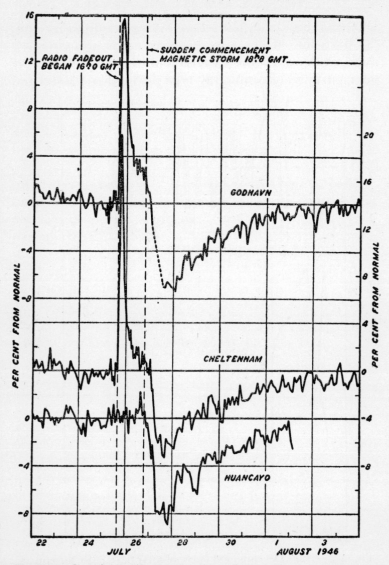

FIG. 9.3.—Cosmic ray increase at time of great flare, 1946 July 25, followed by decrease during great magnetic storm beginning July 26. Reproduced from *Physical Review*, **79**, 501, 1950, by courtesy of the editors and Drs. S. E. Forbush, T. B. Stinchcomb and M. Schein.

somewhat less than the average for the 'ordinary' cosmic ray particles. Wild, as we have seen, has also obtained radio evidence of the expulsion through the corona of solar particles of cosmic ray type during lesser flares.

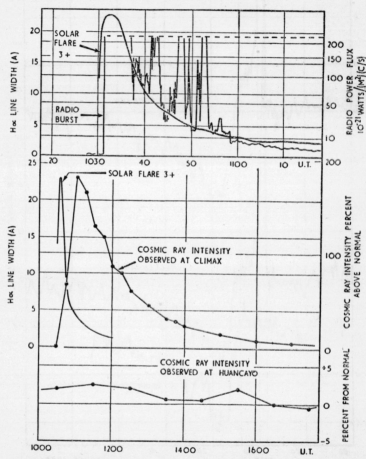

FIG. 9.4.—*Top:* Development curve of solar flare 1949 November 19 (Royal Observatory, Edinburgh) and outburst of radio noise, as recorded by Dr. J. S. Hey on wavelength 4·1 metres. *Bottom:* Development curve of same flare compared with cosmic ray increase observed at Climax (altitude 11,500 ft., magnetic latitude 48° N). No change at Huancayo (altitude 11,000 ft., 1° S).

Two examples of the decreases in cosmic ray intensity which have been observed during great magnetic storms are also visible in Figs. 9.2 and 9.3. At Godhavn on 1942 February 29 the decrease of 10 per cent coincided in time with the onset of a great storm which occurred $19\frac{1}{2}$ hours after the flare. On the other hand, the flare of March 7, believed to have occurred on the sun's limb, generated no magnetic storm, nor was any decrease in cosmic radiation recorded the following day. Once again, on 1946 July 26, a great storm, occurring one day after the flare, was accompanied by a drop in cosmic ray intensity, followed by a gradual return to normal. These circumstances indicate that the influence of the magnetic storm upon cosmic ray intensity is an entirely distinct phenomenon from the sudden increases which occur at the times of the flares. The mechanism is not yet clearly understood. But it seems very probable that the incoming particles are deflected at these times, so that their average energy is reduced through the filtering action of the external magnetic field. According to the theory of Chapman and Ferraro, the external field is established during the storm by the circulation of ions and electrons in the ring-current surrounding the earth.

WHERE FORMED, AND HOW PROPAGATED?

The origin of cosmic rays has remained a great mystery since their discovery in the early years of the century.

Twenty years ago, before the nature of the primary particles was fully understood, theories were fashionable which involved the annihilation of matter in space, leading to the production of high-energy photons, or γ-rays. It is now clear, however, that the primary radiation consists of charged atoms; and, as such, their energies are most probably acquired by accelerations which take place in magnetic or electric fields. The problem is where, and how?

The rapid absorptions which cosmic rays undergo in their passage through the terrestrial atmosphere is proof that they must have their origin in regions where the gas density is extremely low, otherwise they would have no chance of escape and survival. This fact appears to limit their production to the ionized gas clouds of the galaxy, or to the outer atmospheres of the stars. Several theories, based on these considerations, have been proposed in recent times. In that of Fermi the charged atoms are supposed to gain their energies in the cosmic magnetic fields which are now thought to exist in the turbulent clouds of ionized gas within the galaxy, especially in the spiral arms.

The electrical conductivity of the interstellar clouds is believed to be so high that the magnetic lines of force must be 'frozen' into the gas and partake of its turbulent motions. The particles gain their energies through collisions with these moving magnetic fields, and at the same time they are bent into all sorts of random directions, so that they acquire a uniform, or isotropic, distribution within the galactic space. On this view cosmic ray particles are generated within the galaxy and are confined to the galaxy, being unable to escape from its magnetic fields.

Unsöld, on the other hand, has developed the hypothesis that the particles acquire their velocities by the action of rapidly changing electric fields in the chromospheres of the sun and the stars generally. The arrival of solar cosmic rays has only been observed on comparatively few occasions, during the activity associated with great flares, but it is reasonable to suppose that there must be many millions of stars in the galaxy far more 'flare-active' than the sun. If this is so, the contribution of cosmic rays ejected from the stars will be continuous and possibly adequate to maintain the total energy of these particles within the galaxy. Both types of mechanism may play their part; but at present the sun provides our only certain clue.

And so we take our leave of this glorious star upon our door-step. Sunbeams have danced across the threshold throughout the ages; and they promise to sustain our lives on earth for many more. May they continue, likewise, to illuminate the mind of man in his search for understanding of the universe beyond!

Finding the Mass of the Sun in terms of the Earth's Mass

The weight of any object on the earth's surface is simply the earth's attraction for it. From the law of gravitation this is given by

$$W = G.\frac{mM_e}{r^2} \qquad . \qquad . \qquad . \qquad (1)$$

where G is the constant of gravitation, m the mass of the object, M_e the earth's mass and r the earth's radius. The weight may also be written as

$$W = mg \qquad . \qquad . \qquad . \qquad (2)$$

where g is its acceleration when freely falling under gravity. Whence, from (1) and (2) we have

$$g = G.\frac{M_e}{r^2} \qquad . \qquad . \qquad . \qquad (3)$$

Now, the earth is also 'falling' towards the sun, and its acceleration, by analogy from (3), is

$$a = G.\frac{M_s}{R^2} \qquad . \qquad . \qquad . \qquad (4)$$

where M_s is the sun's mass and R is the mean radius of the earth's orbit. The value of this acceleration may be obtained from the formula for circular motion

$$a = \frac{4\pi^2 R}{P^2} \qquad . \qquad . \qquad . \qquad (5)$$

where P is the period of revolution of the earth in its orbit. Hence, from (3), (4) and (5) we have

$$\frac{M_s}{M_e} = \frac{aR^2}{gr^2} = \frac{4\pi^2 R^3}{gP^2r^2}$$

By substitution of the known values of the constants on the right-hand side, we obtain approximately

$$M_s = 332,000\ M_e$$

Radiation Laws and Sun's Temperature

1. The energy distribution within the spectrum from a perfect radiator (black body) is given by Planck's formula

$$E_\lambda = \frac{c_1 \lambda^{-5}}{e^{\frac{c_2}{\lambda T}} - 1}$$

where E_λ is the energy output at any wavelength λ and T is the temperature in degrees absolute. c_1 and c_2 are universal constants whose values are known. The full-line curves of Fig. 1.3 were derived in this manner.

2. Alternatively, the temperature may be derived in terms of the wavelength of maximum energy, λ_{max}, from Wien's law

$$T = k/\lambda_{max}$$

where k is a constant, whose value in angstrom-degree units is $2 \cdot 88 \times 10^8$. Thus, if we take the peak of the solar spectral energy curve to be at 4700 A. we obtain

$$T = 2 \cdot 88 \times 10^8/4700 = 6130° \text{ K.}$$

3. The sun's temperature may also be found from the Stefan-Boltzmann law. This states that the total radiation emitted is proportional to the fourth power of the absolute temperature. If the surroundings of the body are at the absolute zero, the radiation lost per second per unit area of surface is

$$U = \sigma T^4$$

where T is the absolute temperature and σ is a constant. For the sun the value of U (total radiation energy per second from 1 square centimetre of the solar surface) may be derived from the known value of the solar constant (S). The total radiant energy emitted by the *whole of the sun's surface* in one second is the same as the energy received per second on the surface of a sphere, whose radius is the earth's mean distance (R) from the sun, namely $S \times 4\pi R^2/60$ calories. Dividing this by the area of the solar surface, $4\pi A^2$, where A is the sun's radius, we obtain the value for U.

Thus we have
$$\frac{S}{60}\cdot\frac{R^2}{A^2} = U = \sigma T^4$$

whence
$$T = \sqrt[4]{\frac{SR^2}{60\sigma A^2}}$$

and by substitution of the known values, $R = 1\cdot495 \times 10^{13}$ cm., $A = 6\cdot95 \times 10^{10}$ cm., $S = 2\cdot0$ calories per sq. cm. per min., $\sigma = 1\cdot37 \times 10^{-12}$ cal.cm. sec.degree units, we obtain

$$T = 5790^\circ \text{ K.}$$

It may be noted that this radiation temperature is proportional to the fourth root of the solar constant. Thus, if there is an uncertainty of, say, 4 per cent in the measured value of the solar constant, this will cause an uncertainty of only 1 per cent in the value of the derived temperature.

The discrepancy between these various effective temperatures illustrates the extent to which the sun departs from a perfect radiator through limb darkening and other causes.

APPENDIX 3

Zürich Sunspot Numbers for two centuries.
Annual Means

Year	0	1	2	3	4	5	6	7	8	9
1750	**83**	48	48	31	12	10	10	32	48	54
1760	63	**86**	61	45	36	21	11	38	70	**106**
1770	101	82	66	35	31	7	20	92	**154**	126
1780	85	68	38	23	10	24	83	**132**	131	118
1790	90	67	60	47	41	21	16	6	4	7
1800	14	34	45	43	**48**	42	28	10	8	2
1810	0	1	5	12	14	35	**46**	41	30	24
1820	16	7	4	2	8	17	36	50	64	67
1830	**71**	48	28	8	13	57	122	**138**	103	86
1840	63	37	24	11	15	40	62	98	**124**	96
1850	66	64	54	39	21	7	4	23	55	94
1860	**96**	77	59	44	47	30	16	7	37	74
1870	**139**	111	102	66	45	17	11	12	3	6
1880	32	54	60	**64**	64	52	25	13	7	6
1890	7	36	73	**85**	78	64	42	26	27	12
1900	10	3	5	24	42	**63**	54	62	48	44
1910	19	6	4	1	10	47	57	**104**	81	64
1920	38	26	14	6	17	44	64	69	**78**	65
1930	36	21	11	6	9	36	80	**114**	110	89
1940	68	47	31	16	10	33	93	**151**	136	135
1950	83	69	31	13	—	—	—	—	—	—

Years of maximum activity are denoted by heavy type

APPENDIX 4

Calculation of Synodic Rotation Periods for Different Solar Latitudes

The true daily angular motion (ξ) of a point on the solar surface, as found from sunspots (Greenwich), is

$$\xi = 14 \cdot 37° - 2 \cdot 60° \sin^2 \phi \, . \qquad . \quad (1)$$

where ϕ is the solar latitude concerned. Then the true rotation period in days (T) for this latitude will be

$$T = 360°/\xi \quad . \qquad . \qquad . \quad (2)$$

and the synodic period S (time from one central meridian passage to the next) is obtained from the formula

$$\frac{1}{S} = \frac{1}{T} - \frac{1}{E} \quad . \qquad . \qquad . \quad (3)$$

where E is the period of the earth in its orbit, namely 365·26 days.

APPENDIX 5

Radio Power Flux from the Sun

The power emitted at radio wavelength λ (metres) from a perfect radiator (black body) at uniform temperature T degrees absolute is

$$P = \frac{2\pi k T}{\lambda^2} . \Delta f \text{ watts per square metre,}$$

where Δf is the frequency range and k is Boltzmann's constant. The power received from the sun at the earth's distance (R) will, therefore, be

$$P_{\mathrm{E}} = \frac{2\pi k T}{\lambda^2} . \Delta f \left(\frac{r}{R}\right)^2 \text{ watts per square metre,}$$

where r is the sun's radius.

APPENDIX 6

Propagation of Radio Waves in Ionosphere and Corona

The magneto-ionic theory of Appleton determines the possibility of radio wave propagation in all such cases. The refractive index, μ, in a gas containing N free electrons per cubic centimetre is given by

$$\mu^2 = 1 - \frac{4\pi Ne^2}{\varepsilon_0 mp^2}$$

where p is the wave frequency, ε_0 is the permittivity in free space, and e and m are respectively the charge and mass of an electron. This simple formula is applicable only when no magnetic field is present. Propagation of a wave of frequency p is possible so long as $\mu > 1$, that is provided $N < \varepsilon_0 mp^2 / 4\pi e^2$. Since N is known approximately for each coronal level (Baumbach-Allen), the limiting frequency of propagation (p) at each level may be calculated. Only frequencies below this limit can escape.

Bibliography

CHAPTER I

Books

ABBOT, C. G., 1912. *The Sun* (London and New York: Appleton).

BOK, B. J. and BOK, PRISCILLA F., 1946. *The Milky Way*, 2nd edition (London: Churchill).

GAMOW, G., 1941. *The Birth and Death of the Sun* (London: Macmillan).

LANGLEY, S. P. and ABBOT, C. G., 1900. *Annals of the Astrophysical Observatory of the Smithsonian Institution*, I (Washington: Government Printing Office).

SMART, W. M., 1942. *Foundations of Astronomy* (London: Longmans, Green).

SPENCER JONES, H., 1951. *General Astronomy*, 3rd edition (London: Arnold).

WALDMEIER, M., 1946. *Sonne und Erde* (Zürich: Büchergilde Gutenberg).

CHAPTER II

Books

ABETTI, G., 1929. *Solar Physics: Handbuch der Astrophysik*, Band 4 (Berlin: Verlag Julius Springer).

1938. *The Sun* (London: Crosby Lockwood).

BRUHAT, G., 1951. *Le Soleil*, nouvelle édition revue et mise à jour par Lucien d'Azambuja (Paris: Presses Universitaires).

CARRINGTON, R. C., 1863. *Observations of the Spots on the Sun* (London: Williams and Norgate).

KUIPER, G. P. (Editor), 1953. *The Sun* (Chicago: University Press).

MENZEL, D. H., 1949. *Our Sun* (Philadelphia—Toronto: Blakiston).

SECCHI, LE P. A., S.J., 1875. *Le Soleil*, 2ème édition (Paris: Gauthier-Villars).

YOUNG, C. A., 1895. *The Sun* (London: Kegan Paul, Trench, Trübner).

BIBLIOGRAPHY

Papers

BABCOCK, H. W., 1953. 'The Solar Magnetograph', *Astrophys. J.*, **118**, 387.

CORTIE, REV. A. L., S.J., 1921. 'Measurement of Sunspot Positions', *Memoirs of the British Astronomical Association*, **23** (London: Eyre and Spottiswoode).

HALE, G. E. and NICHOLSON, S. B., 1938. *Magnetic Observations of Sunspots*, Parts I and II (Washington: Carnegie Institution).

CHAPTER III

Book

HOYLE, F., 1949. *Some Recent Researches in Solar Physics* (Cambridge: University Press).

Reports and Papers

D'AZAMBUJA, M. et Mme L., 1948. *Étude d'ensemble des protubérances solaires et de leur évolution, Annales de l'Observatoire de Paris*, Tome **6** (Paris: Gauthier-Villars).

HALE, G. E., 1931. 'The Spectrohelioscope and its Work', *Astrophys. J.*, **70**, 265; **71**, 73; **73**, 379; and **74**, 214.

LYOT, B., 1932. 'Étude de la couronne solaire en dehors des éclipses', *Zeit. für Astrophys.*, Band **5**, 73.

PETTIT, E., 1943. 'The Properties of Solar Prominences as related to type', *Astrophys. J.*, **98**, 6.

'Problems of Solar Physics', *Report of the 11th Convegno Volta*, 1952 (Rome: Accademia Nazionale dei Lincei).

SELLERS, F. J., 1952. 'The Sun', *Memoirs of the British Astronomical Association*, **37**.

CHAPTER IV

Book

TERMAN, F. E., 1943. *Radio Engineers' Handbook* (New York and London: McGraw-Hill).

Reports and Papers

ALLEN, C. W., 1946. 'Variation of the Sun's Ultra-violet Radiation as revealed by Ionospheric and Geomagnetic Observations', *Terr. Magn.*, **51**, 1.

APPLETON, SIR EDWARD, 1947. 'The Investigation and Forecasting of Ionospheric Conditions', *Journal of the Institution of Electrical Engineers*, **94**, Part IIIA, No. 11.

APPLETON, E. V. and NAISMITH, R., 1939. 'The Variation of Solar Ultra-violet Radiation during the Sunspot Cycle', *Phil. Mag.*, **27**, 144.

'Report of the Mixed Commission on the Ionosphere'; *I.C.S.U.*, 1948 (Bruxelles: Secrétariat Général de l'U.R.S.I.).

CHAPTER V

Book

LOCKYER, J. N., 1874. *Solar Physics* (London: Macmillan).

Reports and Papers

BRACEWELL, R. N. and STRAKER, T. W., 1949. 'The Study of Solar Flares by means of very long Radio Waves', *Mon. Not. Roy. Astr. Soc.*, **109**, 28.

BUREAU, R., 1950. 'Les renforcements brusques des ondes très longues', *Proc. Phys. Soc.* (B), **63**, 122.

DODSON, HELEN W. and MCMATH, R. R., 1952. 'The Limb Flare of May 8, 1951', *Astrophys. J.*, **115**, 78.

ELLISON, M. A., 1946. 'Visual and Spectrographic Observations of a Great Solar Flare, 1946 July 25', *Mon. Not. Roy. Astr. Soc.*, **106**, 500.

1949. 'Characteristic Properties of Chromospheric Flares', *Mon. Not. Roy. Astr. Soc.*, **109**, 3.

1950. 'Ionospheric Effects of Solar Flares', *Publications of the Royal Observatory, Edinburgh*, **1**, 53.

1952. 'A Photometric Survey of Solar Flares, Plages and Prominences in Hα Light', *Publications of the Royal Observatory, Edinburgh*, **1**, 75.

1953. 'The Hα Radiation from Solar Flares in Relation to Sudden Enhancements of Atmospherics on Frequencies near 27 Kc./s.', *Jour. Atm. Terr. Phys.*, **4**, 226.

GIOVANELLI, R. G., 1948. 'Chromospheric Flares', *Mon. Not. Roy. Astr. Soc.*, **108**, 163.

NEWTON, H. W. and BARTON, H. J., 1937. 'Bright Solar Eruptions and Radio Fadings during the years 1935–36', *Mon. Not. Roy. Astr. Soc.*, **97**, 594.

NICOLET, M., 1943. 'Introduction à l'étude des relations entre les phénomènes solaires et terrestres: le soleil', *Institut Royal Météorologique de Belgique, Miscellanées,* Fasc. **11.**
Relations entre les Phénomènes Solaires et Terrestres (C.I.U.S.), 1948, 1951 (Paris: Hemmerlé, Petit).

CHAPTER VI

Books

CHAPMAN, S., 1936. *The Earth's Magnetism* (London: Methuen).
— and BARTELS, J., 1940. *Geomagnetism* (Oxford: Clarendon Press).

Papers

BARTELS, J., 1932. 'Terrestrial-Magnetic Activity and its Relation to Solar Phenomena', *Terr. Magn.,* **37,** 1.

CHAPMAN, S. and FERRARO, V. C. A., 1931. 'A New Theory of Magnetic Storms', *Terr. Magn.,* **36,** 77 et seq.

GREAVES, W. M. H. and NEWTON, H. W., 1928. 'Magnetic Storms and Solar Activity 1874–1927', *Mon. Not. Roy. Astr. Soc.,* **89,** 84.

1928. 'On the Recurrence of Magnetic Storms', *Mon. Not. Roy. Astr. Soc.,* **89,** 641.

MCINTOSH, D. H., 1951. 'Geomagnetic Solar Flare Effects at Lerwick and Eskdalemuir, and Relationship with Allied Ionospheric Effects', *Jour. Atm. Terr. Phys.,* **1,** 315.

MCNISH, A. G., 1937. 'Terrestrial-Magnetic and Ionospheric Effects associated with Bright Chromospheric Eruptions', *Terr. Magn.,* **42,** 109.

NEWTON, H. W., 1944. 'Solar Flares and Magnetic Storms', *Mon. Not. Roy. Astr. Soc.,* **103,** 244.

1948. 'Geomagnetic "Crochet" Occurrence at Abinger, 1936–46', *Mon. Not. Roy. Astr. Soc., Geophys. Suppl.,* **5,** 200.

1949. 'Observational Aspects of the Sunspot-Geomagnetic Storm Relationships', *Mon. Not. Roy. Astr. Soc., Geophys. Suppl.,* **5,** 321.

SINGER, F. S., MAPLE, E. and BOWEN, W. A., 1951. 'Evidence for Ionospheric Currents from Rocket Experiments near the Geomagnetic Equator', *Jour. Geophys. Res.,* **56,** 265.

CHAPTER VII

Books

ALFVÉN, H., 1950. *Cosmical Electrodynamics* (Oxford: Clarendon Press).
CAPRON, J. R., 1879. *Aurorae: their characters and spectra* (London: Spon).

BIBLIOGRAPHY

FRITZ, H., 1881. *Das Polarlicht* (Leipzig: Brockhaus).

HARANG, L., 1951. *The Aurorae* (London: Chapman and Hall).

Photographic Atlas of Auroral Forms, published by the International Geodetic and Geophysical Union (Oslo, 1930: Brøggers).

TROMHOLT, SOPHUS, 1902. *Catolog der in Norwegen bis Juni 1878 beobachteten Nordlichter* (Oslo: Dybwad).

Ziegler Polar Expedition 1903–1905, Notes and Sketches of the Aurora Borealis by A. Fiala (Washington: National Geographic Society).

Papers

LOVELL, A. C. B., CLEGG, J. A. and ELLYETT, C. D., 1947. 'Radio Echoes from the Aurora Borealis', *Nature*, **160**, 372.

MCLENNAN, J. C. and SHRUM, G. M., 1925. 'On the Origin of the Auroral Green Line', *Proc. Roy. Soc.* (A), **108**, 501.

MEINEL, A. B., 1951. 'Doppler-shifted Auroral Hydrogen Emission', *Astrophys. J.*, **113**, 50.

MONTIGNY, C., 1870. 'Sur la Scintillation et sur son Intensité pendant l'Aurore Boréale observée a Bruxelles', *Academie Royale de Belgique*, Bulletin **29**, 455.

CHAPTER VIII

Books

LOVELL, A. C. B. and CLEGG, J. A., 1952. *Radio Astronomy* (London: Chapman and Hall).

PAWSEY, J. L. and BRACEWELL, R. N., 1954. *Radio Astronomy* (Oxford: Clarendon Press).

Reports and Papers

APPLETON, SIR EDWARD and HEY, J. S., 1946. 'Solar Radio Noise', *Phil. Mag.*, **37**, 73.

HEY, J. S., PARSONS, S. J. and PHILLIPS, J. W., 1948. 'Some Characteristics of Solar Radio Emissions', *Mon. Not. Roy. Astr. Soc.*, **108**, 354.

1949. 'Radio Astronomy', *Mon. Not. Roy. Astr. Soc.*, **109**, 179.

1951. 'Radio Astronomy', *Science Progress*, No. 155, p. 427.

PAWSEY, J. L., 1950. 'Solar Radio-Frequency Radiation', *Proceedings of the Institution of Electrical Engineers*, **97**, 290.

RYLE, M., 1950. 'Radio Astronomy', *Reports on Progress in Physics* (*Physical Society*), **13**, 184.

BIBLIOGRAPHY

VAN DE HULST, H. C., 1951. 'A Course in Radio Astronomy' (Leiden Observatory).

WILD, J. P., 1950. 'Observations of the Spectrum of High-Intensity Solar Radiation at Metre Wavelengths', *Aust. Jour. Sci. Res.* (A), **3,** 399.

CHAPTER IX

Books

JÁNOSSY, L., 1950. *Cosmic Rays*, 2nd edition (Oxford: Clarendon Press).

ROCHESTER, G. D. and WILSON, J. G., 1952. *Atlas of Cloud Chamber Photographs of the Cosmic Radiation* (London: Pergamon Press).

Reports and Papers

BIERMANN, L., 1953. 'Origin and Propagation of Cosmic Rays', *Annual Review of Nuclear Science*, **2,** 335.

DAUDIN, J., 1951. 'Le Soleil et les Rayons Cosmiques', *Relations entre les Phénomènes Solaires et Terrestres* (Septième Rapport, C.I.U.S.).

ELLISON, M. A. and CONWAY, M., 1950. 'The Solar Flare of 1949 November 19', *The Observatory*, **70,** 77.

FERMI, E., 1949. 'On the Origin of the Cosmic Radiation', *Phys. Rev.*, **75,** 1169.

FORBUSH, S. E., STINCHCOMB, T. B. and SCHEIN, M., 1950. 'The Extraordinary Increase of Cosmic-Ray Intensity on November 19, 1949', *Phys. Rev.*, **79,** 501.

NEHER, H. V. and ROESCH, W. C., 1948. 'Cosmic Ray Effects from Solar Flares and Magnetic Storms', *Rev. Mod. Phys.*, **20,** 350.

SWAN, W. F. G., 1954. 'The Story of Cosmic Rays', *Sky and Telescope*, February–July.

UNSÖLD, A., 1949. 'Über den Ursprung der Radiofrequenzstrahlung und der Ultrastrahlung in der Milchstrasse', *Zeit. für Astrophys.*, **26,** 176.

Index

Abbot, C. G., 18, 93
Abetti, G., 50
Adams, N., 210
Aerials of high gain, 182
Alfvén, H., 51, 52, 83, 175
Allen, C. W., 84, 94, 95, 160, 189, 224
Appleton, E. V., 3, 21, 88, 93, 109, 143, 184, 194, 224
Aristotle, 161
Atmospherics, sudden enhancements of, 102, 121, 123, 125
Aurorae, 161 et seq.: colours of, 166; daylight, 178; distribution and frequency of, 168; early records of, 161; earth currents, 176; forms of, 164; noise from, 177; photography of, 171; position and height of, 170; relation to sunspot cycle, 169; scintillation of stars during, 178; spectrum of, 171; theories of, 173

Baade, W., 30
Babcock, H. W., 55
Banwell, C. J., 194
Barnett, M. A. F., 88
Bartels, J., 141, 147, 148, 159
Baumbach, S., 189, 224
Bennington, T. W., 105
Bethe, H., 27
Birkeland, K., 150, 174
Bjerknes, V., 51
Black body radiation, 14
Bolton, J. G., 194, 196
Bondi, H., 82
Bowen, W. A., 142
Bracewell, R. N., 102, 122, 127
Braddick, H. J. J., 210
Breit, G., 88

Bruce, C. E. R., 131
Brück, H. A., 156
Brück, Mrs. H. A., 14
Budden, K. G., 122
Bureau, R., 121

Camden, W., 162
Carrington, R. C., 112
Chapman, S., 140, 141, 144, 153, 154, 155, 173, 174, 213
Chree, C., 159
Christiansen, W. N., 187, 193
Chromosphere: general, 12, 57; observation of, 63; temperature of, 13
Clay, J., 205
Clegg, J. A., 176
Cloud chamber, 204
Cockcroft, J., 25
Cooke, A., 1
Corona: general, 13, 75; continuous spectrum of, 78; emission lines of, 79, 80; nature of, 77; rays, 84; refraction of radio waves by, 198; relation to M-storms, 84; structure related to prominences, 84; temperature of, 78; theories of formation of, 82, 83
Coronagraph, 76
Corpuscular streams, 155, 174
Cosmic noise fadeout, 126
Cosmic rays: decreases during magnetic storms, 213; distribution in latitude and azimuth, 205; increases associated with flares, 129, 208; methods of recording, 203; primary radiation, 200; secondary radiation, 201; variations in time, 206

231

INDEX

Critical frequencies of ionospheric
layers, 89
Crochet, magnetic, 118, 119, 137,
144
Crommelin, A. M., 85

d'Azambuja, L., 69
d'Azambuja, Mme M., 69, 112
Dellinger, J. H., 104, 120
Deslandres, H., 60
Development curves: of flares, 114;
of ionospheric effects, 119
Dobson, G. M. B., 97
Dodson, H., 116
Doppler effect, 60

Earth's magnetism, 134 et seq.:
character figures, 146; crochets,
144; daily variation of, 138; disturbance of, 145; effect on cosmic
rays, 205; K-indices, 146; magnetic storms, 148; M-storms and
flare storms, 150; overhead currents, 140; theories of magnetic
storms, 150; theories of overhead
currents, 142; unsteadiness (U),
146
Eccles, W. H., 87
Eddington, A., 7, 23
Edlén, B., 79
Egedal, J., 169
Einstein, A., 24
Electron concentration: corona, 189;
ionosphere, 91
Ellyett, C. D., 176
Energy, source of sun's, 22
Evans, J. W., 61
Evershed, J., 49, 50

Fabricius, J., 37
Faculae, 45
Fermi, E., 214
Ferraro, V. C. A., 153, 154, 155,
173, 213
Flare stars, 133
Flares: classification and properties
of, 111; delayed effects of, 128;

development of, 113; flare surges,
116; line-width and central intensity, 114; nature of, 110; particles
blown out from, 128; radio noise
from, 127, 191, 195; spectra of,
112; stellar flares, 132; terrestrial
effects of, 116; theories of, 130
Forbes, J. D., 178
Forbush, S. E., 209, 210, 211
Fraunhofer, J., 12
Fraunhofer absorption lines, 12;
profiles of, 64
Fritz, H., 161, 164, 167, 179

Galaxy, sun's place in, 28
Galileo, G., 3, 37
Gamow, G., 25
Gassendi, P., 163
Gauss, C. F., 134
Geiger-Müller counter, 203
Gilbert, W., 56, 134
Giovanelli, R. G., 131, 175
Granulation, 31
Greaves, W. M. H., 150
Grotrian, W., 79

Hale, G. E., 2, 46, 47, 48, 50, 54, 60,
110
Halley, E., 163
Harang, L., 171, 173
Heaviside, O., 87
Helmholtz, H. von, 22
Hey, J. S., 3, 184, 192, 194, 195, 208
Hirayama, S., 39
Hodgson, R., 112
Holmes, A., 23
Hoyle, F., 74, 82, 175
Hulbert, E. O., 159
Hydrogen emission from flares, 156

Ionosphere: critical frequencies of
layers, 89; D-, E- and F-layers of,
90; disturbance by flares, 101;
disturbance by solar particles,
109; exploration of, 87; forecasting conditions in, 104; influence
of sunspot cycle on, 106; propa-

232